SCIENCE, FAITH AND SCEPTICISM

SCIENCE, FAITH
and
SCEPTICISM

by

JOHN LEWIS

1959
LAWRENCE & WISHART
LONDON

Printed in Great Britain by
The Camelot Press Ltd., London and Southampton

WHAT THIS BOOK IS ABOUT

ONE of the great controversies of our time is about the possibility of metaphysics. This term has had a number of different meanings, but in the debate now proceeding it means two things:

Firstly, speculation concerned with matters beyond possible human experience—God, the Absolute, or any other transcendental reality which may be supposed in some way to affect or control this earthly life.

Secondly, the formulation of some theory of the nature of reality, and some explanation of the significance of human life, passing beyond what can be concluded from the unorganised and unsystematised data of ordinary, everyday experience.

Many contemporary philosophers, refusing to pass beyond the concrete data of experience, emphatically deny the possibility of metaphysics in the first sense and they therefore reject all methods of reaching transcendental truth. But the philosophical method they adopt also compels them to reject the possibility of reaching any general theory of existence. In some cases, indeed, their method of reasoning has even carried them as far as denying the objective reality of scientific law and scientific theory as descriptive of external reality.

It is the argument of this book that while the criticism of other-worldly speculation is entirely justified, this criticism does not involve us in the rejection of scientific truth, nor does it preclude the formulation of theories of human life.

If it did, then philosophy would indeed be completely nihilistic — destructive of every kind of world view as well as of the validity of science. This is the inevitable consequence of so drastic a scepticism.

Now the critical method advanced by the philosophers who go thus far is a most useful one if its limits are realised. It eliminates not only all sorts of supernatural and mythological explanations of existence but all those philosophies of life which are not based on scientific thinking.

But its excessive zeal and mistaken logic are exposed when it lumps together scientific theory and metaphysical explanation, and rejects both.

If we can restrain this zeal and correct the logic we shall see how science establishes its theories and also how we can establish with equal validity theories as to the meaning of human life.

But such a method will prove as exacting in this wider sphere as it is in science itself. We only begin to theorise usefully about life when we have learnt how to avoid the pitfalls of illegitimate speculation, when indeed we have painfully *unlearnt* a great many mistakes and a great many fallacious methods of thinking.

But when we have come through it is immensely worth while. To have no philosophy of life is as bad as to have a false one. To have a well-grounded interpretation of the meaning of existence is what most people would value above everything.

What kind of philosophy would that be?

Not something vague and general, however lofty in sentiment or heroic in aim.

Not something totally explanatory, authoritative and final.

It will inevitably be but partial truth and very incomplete—in process indeed of continuous revision and reformulation.

It will be concerned with life in the world to-day, and such generalisations as it advances must concern the world of social struggle as well as the problems of personal life. It will be alarmingly concrete and therefore cannot avoid being controversial. It will be not above the battle, like so many philosophies, but in it.

And so philosophy, and science too, like all honest thinking about the real world cannot but be partisan. That does not mean that it is prejudiced or wilfully adopts a sectional or partial point of view. But it does mean that it cannot avoid coming to conclusions on some of the most hotly debated issues in the modern world. Impartiality does not mean the permanent suspension of judgment either in the courts of law or philosophy.

J. L.

CONTENTS

CONTENTS

CHAPTER ONE

METAPHYSICS AND MYSTIFICATION

Two Roads to Truth

ONE of the most urgent questions for modern thought is whether the method of reasoning which has proved its adequacy in every field of scientific enquiry from physics to archaeology is, in principle, applicable to the problems of human life, or whether scientific thought is by its very nature limited to the merely physical.

It is the latter point of view which is now being urged in many quarters in an endeavour to keep these questions from scientific treatment. It is argued that there are two distinct orders of truth—one which deals with the material and measureable: scientific truth, and another which proceeds by a higher faculty than that of scientific reason and apprehends spiritual realities.

This may be called "The Two Truths Theory".

The acceptance of this theory requires us to abandon the method of observation, hypothesis and verification, which serves us so well in scientific matters, and make use either of the method of mystical intuition or metaphysical reasoning (whether that be philosophical or theological).

The assumption is that in dealing with those aspects of human existence which concern the nature and destiny of man these are the only reliable roads to truth. This, however, is open to serious question.

Can We Trust Our Intuitions?

In every field of thought the first question is how do we sift truth from falsehood. Whether it is a scientific hypothesis, a philosophical theory or a spiritual intuition, how can you be sure that you are right? How can you avoid error?

In science, as we know, there are well established methods of experiment and observation, and these have abundantly proved their worth; but it is not sufficiently recognised that *intuition* also requires verification. It is not enough that we *feel* an overwhelming sense of its truth. Spiritual conviction of this sort, if there is no method of checking its validity, lays us wide open to the perils of subjectivism, of pure delusion.

The second road to truth is clearly not the straight and narrow path of indubitable enlightenment that is generally assumed. In the first place, if *my* intuition reveals truth as it exists for *me*, is it by any means certain that the intuitions of other people will reveal the same truth? The implications of such a position have been clearly perceived by Aldous Huxley. "No psychological experience," he says, "is 'truer', so far as we are concerned, than any other. Science is no 'truer' than common sense; or lunacy than art or religion. Every man has as good a right to his own particular world-view as to his own particular kidneys . . . there is a very intimate connection between a man's vision and his philosophy." A philosophy, he argues, is not an account of the universe, it is the symptom of a state of mind. "A man may be born with a strong tendency to inhabit one kind of universe rather than another."[1] We possess private universes; the world is in us; we are not in the world—one world, the same for all of us.

The full significance of this subjectivism is not always realised because the "truths" we are considering are often remote metaphysical abstractions, helpful ideals or consoling hopes for the ultimate triumph of right. But men can have intuitive convictions of racial superiority, or of the sanctity of class privilege. They can be so convinced of the truth of their religious beliefs that they want to burn all heretics. They may believe, intuitively, that their sacred egoism is the last word. From passionately held but unprovable convictions come holy wars, race murder, the colour bar, the

---

[1] Aldous Huxley, *Do What You Will.*

justification of unbridled egoism, the assertion of the unquestioned superiority of aristocratic cliques or fanatical
sects, the sanctification of class privilege. *for all as in Communism!*

The Mystic Vision

Recently there have been far-reaching claims for the
effects of such drugs as mescalin on our powers to apprehend
spiritual truths,[1] based on no more substantial grounds than
the psychological experience of revelation and ecstacy produced by the effects of these chemicals on the brain.

It is in dealing with nonsense of this sort that the logical
methods of contemporary philosophy are of real help. Professor Ayer points out that these mystical "experiences" are
of course real enough, but "in describing his vision the
mystic does not give us any information about the external
world; he merely gives us indirect information about the
condition of his own mind."[2] And when we are told that he
has received a revelation about the nature of ultimate reality
which transcends human understanding, this can only mean
that it is unintelligible, that is to say meaningless. Nor can
the mystic tell us what these truths are that he has discovered,
and therefore it is impossible for us to see how far they are in
harmony with the facts of life. Since he is unable to produce
any intelligible propositions we are surely justified in saying
that he has said nothing at all about reality. "It is no use his
saying that he has apprehended facts but is unable to express
them. For we know that if he really had acquired any information he would be able to express it. He would be able to
indicate in some way or another how the genuineness of his
discovery might be empirically determined. The fact that he
cannot reveal what he 'knows' or even himself devise an
empirical test to validate his 'knowledge', shows that his
state of mystical intuition is not a genuinely cognitive state."[3]
In fact it looks as though he were trying to sell us something
the nature of which unfortunately cannot be divulged.

[1] Aldous Huxley, *The Doors of Perception.*
[2] Ayer, *Language, Truth and Logic.*   [3] Ibid.

Delusion and Reality

Psychology throws a flood of light upon both the form and content of these revelations which come flooding into consciousness in such overwhelming fashion. Delusions, hallucinations, voices, visions, extraordinary physical feelings, all these are perfectly well known to the psychiatrist who can distinguish them without much difficulty from the activities of the normal mind.[1] What is so characteristic of this type of experience is that it feels like an invasion from without—it is not *us*. The readiness with which, while dreaming, we accept the incidents of a vivid dream as objective facts is probably the best illustration we can have of what an acute hallucinated state must be like.

The unconscious mind can hold, formulate and subsequently give forth for expression, ideas, images, emotions and associations of ideas which have never been consciously recognised or entertained for one instant—even on the fringe of personal consciousness. That is why in their subsequent emergence from the unconscious they seem wholly foreign to the very mind that has just given them birth. What convinces the surprised subject is precisely the *otherness* of this subliminal uprush, which therefore seems to him either a communication or an objective perception of something outside himself.

Abnormal states which arise from paranoia or some other condition of mental unbalance, are not the only form of delusion. Delusions also result from some infective or poisoning process, such as that produced by mescalin, and other drugs. These are called toxic psychoses.

No trained psychologist has ever met with a case of voices, blinding revelation, divine communication or trance medium phenomena that could not be accounted for by chemical, organic or psychological causes.

The Beyond that is Within

An excellent example of spiritual revelation given to these

[1] See Hart, *The Psychology of Insanity*, and the Pelican, *To Define True Madness*, by Yellowlees.

higher faculties of the soul is to be found in Dr. Kenneth Walker's recent book on Ouspensky.[1] He speaks of religious revelation as consisting of "an utter conviction that behind all outward appearances there is a supreme reality." The discovery of this brings with it "a sense of joyous liberation from the tyranny of personality. At the same time there is no desire to explain the reason of this or to describe what is happening." The intellect is silenced. "In the presence of the eternal and the divine everything which before had seemed of such importance, our own interests, and our safety, our own likes and dislikes were of no account. All that we know for certain is that we are in the presence of a great truth, in the presence of holiness, and that we must live in harmony with it." "The simple affirmation that there exists a spiritual world which penetrates the visible and tangible world" is all we need to pilot us through life. " 'Lead kindly light, amid the encircling gloom. Lead thou me on.' "

It is difficult to know exactly what this means. We have been told by philosophers that to develop a thought's meaning we should see what difference believing it would make to what we do. The difference indicates the real meaning of the idea.

Now the only effect of these ideas that I can imagine would be an apathetic acquiescence in the evils and injustices of the world, a disinclination either to understand or to control the world, and a gradual cessation of all intelligent thought. This might be a very satisfactory formula for securing the docile compliance of men with the dictator of a totalitarian régime.

T. S. Eliot once declared that the study of Indian metaphysics left him in a state of enlightened mystification. When the vision of the eternal dawns, he tells us, effort and exploration are forgotten in the sense of the Absolute; living becomes the discovery of the already known; beginning and end are one. History is a pattern of timeless moments.

This too sounds impressive and profound, but if it means anything at all it means that we must accept things as they

[1] Kenneth Walker, *Meaning and Purpose*.

are, achieving a total tolerance in which evil and perversity are endured for the sake of the insight they ultimately generate.

> "Time present and time past
> Are both perhaps present in time future
> And time future contained in time past
> If all time is eternally present,
> All time is unredeemable."

Enough has been said to show that spiritual intuition cannot be trusted as a higher road to truth. Intuition can play an indispensable part in the formation of hypothesis, but in such cases, as we shall show, it is absolutely necessary to *test* the hypothesis. When intuition is advanced as the second road to truth it is relied on in itself and without verification. It is this that opens the door to every kind of delusion and superstition.

The Quest of Metaphysics

A different approach to transcendental reality, is offered by certain forms of philosophy and theology. Although these systems have a strongly rational element, they too, lack any reliable method of bringing their theories to the test of truth.

As an example we may take the usual theological argument for a *First Cause*. It runs like this: We think of the whole sequence of events as an endless chain of cause and effect; but we cannot imagine this going back for ever. There is a logical necessity for some originating power or cause. This we call the First Cause to distinguish it from the others which were themselves in turn effects and are therefore known as "secondary causes". This first cause is God.

Further, all physical events are so bound together that they are what they are only because of the whole complex of which they are a part. No single event can be taken as the cause of the system, which must therefore be outside the system—this is the First Cause. It is the source of all other causes, a self-determining cause.

This argument no longer has the force that it once had.

So distinguished a theologian as Dean Inge, for example, rejects it. "It is most unreasonable," he says, "to expect philosophy to answer the questions why the world was made, and how it was made. We must take the world as we find it."[1] And even the great medieval thinker Thomas Aquinas concluded that reason would be compelled to admit the eternity of the physical world, an eternal sequence of cause and effect, but for the biblical revelation which tells us that the physical world was created.

There is no logical compulsion to accept a Cause of the system of causes, there is no necessity to seek for the first *whence* and the last *whither* of the whole cosmic process. The only sensible questions about the world are concerned with what we can do with it and in it, what purposes we can realise within the scope of human effort.

If it is not possible to speak of the First Cause of the Universe does this mean that our lives and human history have no meaning?

What it means is that there can be no meaning of this sort in the world prior to us and apart from us. What meaning there is in existence is the meaning *we* give to it. Our lives have whatever purpose we succeed in putting into them. There is no evidence for asserting that the universe as a whole fulfils any ulterior purpose.

Kant and Metaphysics

The philosopher Kant developed a powerful argument against all those total explanations which, in terms of a greater reality standing behind the order of nature, seek to provide us with a summary answer to all problems.

Kant argued that human experience allows only partial and conditional explanations concerned with the sequence of events in time. A false metaphysic tries to apply our categories of explanation outside all possible experience. If you think of the fact of existence itself as a mystery, then you will soon find yourself looking for an explanation of the universe outside the

[1] W. R. Inge, *Contemporary British Philosophy*.

universe itself; in other words, you will look for a transcendental explanation—for something beyond all existence which explains why anything at all exists.

Any summary conclusion, jumping from our conviction of the existence of an order of nature to the easy assumption that there is an ultimate reality which, in some unexplained way, is to be appealed to for the removal of perplexity, is not a great philosophical achievement but a great refusal of rationality and of intellectual integrity. We have rather to search whether nature does not in its very being show itself as self-explanatory. The sheer statement of what things are may contain the real explanation of why things are.

Kant's *Critique of Pure Reason* is designed not to discredit science or reason, but to show that the limits of sense experience are the limits of all sound reasoning about the world. But reason divorced from sense experience cannot get us very far. It cannot give us knowledge of the metaphysical objects philosophy constantly seeks and if we persist in doing so the result is mere sophistry. Above all, there can be no metaphysical theory of the universe as a whole, nor can we possibly prove the existence of God.

That is why metaphysics seems incapable of any settled results and its history is a record, not of steady progress, but of bewildering marches and counter-marches. The confident conclusions of one philosopher are as confidently denied by another, and the endless indecisive conflict produces the conviction that in philosophy one doctrine is as good as another and therefore none are worth very much.

To use Kant's own words: "Metaphysic, a completely isolated and speculative science of reason, which declines all teaching of experience, and rests on concepts only, in which reason therefore is meant to be her own pupil, has hitherto not been so fortunate as to enter on the secure path of a science. It cannot be denied therefore, that the method of metaphysic has hitherto consisted in groping only, and, what is the worst, in groping among mere concepts."

System-building of the old kind, has never recovered from

Kant's criticism. We cannot discover by pure reason what *must* have been the origin of things, and what *must* be the structure of the universe, nor can we by seeking find these timeless realities by means of which to explain the purposes of human life. It is a basic error to transfer to the whole field of existence the kind of question which is only legitimate within experimental areas within that field. It is perfectly reasonable to ask what is the cause of any particular event or for an explanation of geological phenomena or the sequence of animal forms in evolution; but it is not reasonable to ask for the cause of the totality of events, of the world-as-a-whole. The legitimate question is concerned with causal relations within the world system. The illegitimate question looks for something *outside* that system to explain it.

Suppose that it is asserted that there is an over-riding purpose, a total explanation, which accounts for everything that happens so that there neither is nor could be any event not so determined. Then, of course, nothing that occurred could count against the theory, and nothing could count in its favour. It would therefore appear that it makes no difference whether we believe in it or deny it. There can be no argument in the field of pure reason, because there is no way of either proving or disproving propositions of this kind.

The Irrefutability of Magic

An interesting example of this type of reasoning is found among primitive people who believe in magic, for instance the Azande of the Southern Sudan.[1] Any misfortune is attributed to witchcraft and these people have built up a complex system of beliefs and rites which make sense only when they are seen as interdependent parts of a whole. Granted certain postulates, everything that happens illustrates and confirms the belief. Nor is it possible for anything to happen which contradicts the belief. Witchcraft causes death. Therefore a death is evidence of witchcraft, and the oracles confirm that witchcraft caused it. Magic is made to avenge

[1] E. E. Evans-Pritchard, *Witchcraft, Oracles and Magic Among the Azande.*

B

the death. A neighbour dies soon afterwards and he is obviously the guilty person and has been punished. If a spell fails to work that proves that the words were not uttered correctly or that some part of the rite was not faithfully carried out.

If rain-making ceremonies have been carried out, the desired event is almost certain to take place sooner or later and it would then appear that the rite was the cause of the event. A ceremony intended to make the wind blow or to work the death of an enemy will always be followed ultimately by the occurrence it was meant to bring to pass. "Similarly, rites observed in the morning to help the sun to rise, and in spring to wake the dreaming earth from her winter sleep, will invariably appear to be crowned with success. . . . Hence the practical savage, with his conservative instincts, might well turn a deaf ear to the subtleties of the theoretical doubter, the philosophical radical, who presumed to hint that sunrise and spring might not after all, be direct consequences of the punctual performance of certain daily or yearly ceremonies, and that the sun might perhaps continue to rise and trees to blossom though the ceremonies were occasionally intermitted, or even discontinued altogether."[1]

If in such a closed system of thought a belief is contradicted by a particular experience, this merely shows that the experience was mistaken, or inadequate, or the contradiction is accounted for by secondary elaborations of belief which provide satisfactory explanations of the apparent inconsistency.

Thus the system is completely proof against being discredited by any facts whatsoever.

Now as a principle of scientific method it is impermissible to advance a hypothesis which is incapable of verification in actual experience. It must be possible to recognise the state of affairs which would prove the theory and the state of affairs which would disprove it. If belief is so conceived that it is compatible with no matter what facts of observation then this is an illegitimate form of thinking. This is in fact the form

[1] Frazer, *The Golden Bough*.

characteristic of all animistic, theological and metaphysical theories.

No Road but that of Science

To sum up: It would appear that *there is no second road to truth*, whether by intuition, speculative metaphysics, theological reasoning or dreaming up comforting illusions. There is no privileged short cut to truth. It has never been found possible to substantiate in any way the existence of a transcendental purpose, a supernatural reality, miraculous interventions in human affairs, or spiritual guidance for mankind.

If these roads are closed what is left open to us? We have the methods which are valid in the natural sciences, and which are applied with success in the fields of psychology, anthropology and sociology. If in these departments we can construct wide ranging theories which can be submitted to rigorous tests, does this not indicate that knowledge depends not on finding ways to truth which evade the methods of scientific thinking, but precisely in applying them, always of course with such modifications as the special fields demand, while retaining the basic criteria of the experimental approach. *There is only one road to Truth.*

CHAPTER TWO

HARD FACTS AND SCIENTIFIC THEORIES

Locke and the Empiricists

THE rejection of metaphysical speculation and unverified intuition as royal roads to truth is not new in philosophy. John Locke (1632-1704), who was profoundly dissatisfied with the muddle and confusion for which illegitimate methods of thinking were responsible, endeavoured in his *Essay Concerning Human Understanding* to set forth the *limits* of human reasoning. He argued that truth must be limited to what can be deduced from or logically constructed from sense experience; that the unerring mark of love of truth is "not entertaining any proposition with greater assurance than the proof it is built upon will warrant", so that the degree of assent we give to any view will depend upon the grounds of probability in its favour. Since metaphysical speculations and theological dogmas have no such support they should not be entertained. If such hypotheses are accepted as real truths we shall find ourselves "living in a sort of waking dream", which leads only to "a learned ignorance".

The Limitations of Human Knowledge

Such knowledge does not compete in the sweep of its generalisations or the grandeur of its conceptions with the great speculative systems of philosophy. "All those sublime thoughts which tower above the clouds, and reach as high as heaven itself, take their rise and footing here; in all that great extent wherein the mind wanders in those remote speculations it may seem to be elevated with, it stirs not one jot beyond

those ideas which sense or reflection have offered for its contemplation."[1] But it is the only antidote of permanent value
to the outbreaks of mysticism, irrationalism, confused verbalis-
ing and pretentious profundity by which philosophers are in-
fected from time to time.

John Locke lived at a time in some ways like our own in its
outbursts of religious feeling and the resort to emotional and
instinctive grounds for belief, "an opinionated self-confidence
engendered by a supposed inner illumination." His criticism
of this tendency is as valid to-day as ever it was, and as
appropriate. He tried to separate reasonable convictions from
"inclinations, fancies and strong assurances" which deny
reason and substitute for it "the ungrounded fancies of a
man's own brain, and assumed them for a foundation both of
opinion and conduct." He roundly condemned what he called
"illumination without search, and certainty without proof."
All this is of great and permanent value in Locke and was
influential not only in this country but in France where it
provided a powerful impulse to the French Enlightenment.

"We can by speech and pen make men more enlightened
and better." So wrote Voltaire. He was not a profound
thinker, but he admired Locke immensely and assimilated his
ideas, and became a most effective populariser of the new
philosophy among the reading public. The ideas were new
and revolutionary; the age was one of transition; and his
critical thinking suited the times.

The French *philosophes* were men of genius, clear-headed
and acute. Their influence on their generation was profound.
For a thousand years Europe had been a prey to intolerant,
intolerable visionaries and dogmatists. The common sense of
such thinkers as Diderot, D'Alembert, Voltaire, Helvetius and
Holbach, their grasp of the obvious facts of human suffering,
their hatred of hocus-pocus, acted on the world like a bath of
moral and intellectual cleansing. We cannot overrate the
debt of gratitude which we owe to these men.

It was a case not only of reason versus unreason, but a

[1] Locke, *Essay Concerning Human Understanding.*

sceptical reason versus speculative reason, that is to say, versus the reason which built up an entire philosophy of existence out of the first principles derived from rational intuition and pure logic. Locke and Hume were the great protaganists of this sceptical attitude in Britain, and now the spirit of criticism spread to France.

"We must not say," said Voltaire, "let us begin by inventing principles whereby we may be able to explain everything; rather we must say, let us make an exact analysis of the matter, and then we shall try to see, with much diffidence, if it fits in with any principle. . . . It is given to us to calculate, to weigh, to measure, to observe; this is natural philosophy; almost all the rest is chimera."

The philosophers of the French Enlightenment directed their attack first against the Church and then against society. They inaugurated a new era in European thought and prepared the ground for the French Revolution and for Marxism. "The French materialists did not limit their criticism to matters of religious belief; they extended it to whatever scientific tradition or political institution they met with";[1] and gave their doctrine a universal application.

"Men will never be free," said Diderot, "until the last king is strangled with the entrails of the last priest." Rejecting in the name of reason the notion of a pre-established, immovable, eternal order they strengthened the rising bourgeoisie in its struggle against feudalism. They believed that since all evils are due to superstition, ignorance and the vicious and baseless conceptions of a corrupt governing class, education and enlightenment could expose their claims, discredit their authority and reform society.

Scepticism and Metaphysics

In England Hume was pressing scepticism even farther. He divided permissible statements into mathematical truths and matters of fact. "When we run through our libraries, persuaded of these principles, what havoc must we make? If

[1] Engels, *Socialism, Utopian and Scientific*.

we take in our hand any volume, of divinity or school meta-physics, for instance, let us ask: Does it contain any abstract reasoning, concerning quantity or number? No. Does it contain any experimental reasoning concerning matter of fact and existence? No. Commit it then to the flames, for it can contain nothing but sophistry and illusion."[1]

Lord Bolingbroke, from whom Pope derived all his philo-sophical ideas, did a great deal to spread this sceptical spirit in English society. He speaks of the fallacy and impertinence of a philosophy which treats the creatures of the mind as subsistent entities. "This philosophy has rolled down a torrent of chimerical knowledge from pagan and Christian antiquity, with little opposition, and scarce any interruption, to the present age; for which reason it is as necessary to expose the futility of this philosophy, as it would have been many centuries ago."

There follows an interesting argument very much in line with the approach of contemporary philosophy. The meta-physical philosopher, says Bolingbroke, is very little concerned with scientific fact. "Metaphysics served his purpose better. Hypotheses of the former kind (i.e. scientific) must be founded in some real knowledge; how high soever the top of the ladder reaches, the foot must stand firm on earth. But hypotheses of the other kind (i.e. metaphysical) are more easy to be framed, and less easy to be controlled . . . they are not content to account for what may be by what is, nor to improve science according to the conditions of our nature, by raising proba-bility on the foundations of certainty; but the makers of them effect to range in the immense void of possibility, with little or no regard to actuality; and begin very often, as well as end, in supposition. Not only their systems are hypothetical, but the first principles of them, and the very ideas and notions which compose them are hypothetical too."[2]

Bentham and the Utilitarians later continued the struggle

[1] Hume, *An Enquiry Concerning Human Understanding*.

[2] See Pope's *Essay on Man* and the excellent account of it in Laird's *Philosophy in the English Poets*.

along their own lines. They were prepared to accept nothing that was not based on experience; Mill's *Logic* was intended to explain what constituted proof in our search for general ideas, how we know when a proposition is true, and how by *induction* we can proceed from facts to scientific laws. He, too, rejected intuition as a way to truth. He regarded the claim to apprehend truth by a special spiritual faculty as the greatest speculative hindrance to the regeneration of society, which, he believed, could never be effected under the influence of a philosophy which makes opinions their own proof and feelings their own justification.

Scepticism and the Return to Faith

But this purely negative approach had the effect of encouraging in a different direction the very beliefs it was engaged in criticising. Even Hume himself is dissatisfied, and after breaking down by his appeal to experience the rational defence of both religion and science he was compelled to show that habit and custom are the real guarantees of both. But if we cannot believe on the basis of reason we must believe on the basis of faith; and, as Pierre Bayle said, such faith is all the more glorious in proportion as the doctrine that is believed is contrary to reason!

Empiricism and Modern Science

Modern science owes much to empiricism, to exclusive concern with observation and experiment. The steady advance of such enquiry, its extension to living things, the achievement of evolutionary theory, the development of bio-chemistry have steadily extruded supernaturalism and "vital forces" from nature as science conceives it.

To-day there is no widespread belief of an effectual kind in the impact of a supernatural world upon this one. If the wireless set goes wrong, or the car breaks down, if one's child runs a temperature or shows other symptoms of illness, if insect pests ruin the crops, we look for material not spiritual causes of these mishaps. We even look for the psychological causes of mental sickness, of child delinquency, of an anxiety neurosis, of sexual abnormality or a strained marriage relationship. We increasingly believe that there are reasons for things which it is the business of science to find out. Mysticism still confuses many, still holds up useful lines of enquiry and advance, is still responsible for crooked thinking, and we must not weaken our criticism, but rather intensify it. But supernaturalism is on the retreat.

Sir Herbert Read has argued that "the ever increasing fund of scientific knowledge about the universe and the process of historical evolution has become so diffused that the criticism of supernaturalism which was formerly found in only a minority of intellectual heretics is now universal. I would also suggest that the actual character of this knowledge has become more positive and inclusive, leaving very little to be ascribed to the agency of a supernatural power. As a result, the minority (as it actually is) of believers, in advanced civilisations, now consists of the very ignorant and the very clever."[1]

What is the Method of Science?

Yet exponents of the "higher road to truth" are at pains to show that the disciplined and factual procedures of science so limit its scope as to exclude indubitable aspects of reality. On what grounds do they support this point of view?

The argument depends firstly on presenting scientific method as concerned solely with physics and chemistry, that is with the measureable, excluding life and mind, which, it is assumed, science reduces without remainder to the physical. Secondly it has to show that scientific reasoning is a strict process of deduction excluding imagination and intuitive thoughts. In other words the scientific method is mechanistic and therefore whatever it handles must appear mechanical too. If this were so, then clearly wide ranges of truth would be inaccessible to scientific reasoning and another road to truth would have to be found.

(1) But science is by no means confined to the measureable.

[1] Herbert Read, *A Coat of Many Colours*.

"The part played by measurement and quantity in science," says Bertrand Russell, "is very great, but is, I think, sometimes overestimated. Qualitative laws can be as scientific as quantitative ones." Nor is science limited to physics and chemistry, but it suits the advocates of a higher road to truth to think so. It is indeed necessary for them to exhibit science as by its very nature limited in order to prepare the stage for the entry of a higher form of knowledge.

But not only is the scope of science wide enough to include biology and psychology, economics and anthropology, sociology and history, but its methods are capable of modification to suit each field of study.

What makes reasoning scientific is firstly the method of observation, experiment and analysis, and secondly the framing of hypotheses and their subsequent testing. This procedure is valid in any field and is not restricted to the physical sciences.

(2) In so far as this criticism assumes that science does not make use of the imagination but is concerned with purely deductive logical processes, it is very far from understanding the working of the scientific mind. Far from excluding imagination and intuition the scientist cannot frame his hypothesis without them. Often the scientific mind makes a leap to a new truth, by what unconscious reasonings or lightning induction the psychologist may help us to understand.

What science rules out is not intuition but untested intuition, the taking of the intuition itself as sufficient evidence for its own truth. For science, what is perceived intuitively must then be tested by observation, experiment and reasoning, and only accepted if it passes these tests.

The Nature of Scientific Hypothesis

In what respects does a scientific hypothesis differ from those philosophical systems and religious theories which seek to provide a coherent and unifying explanation of the facts of life?

The difference lies in the fact that science subjects its hypotheses to experimental tests. If this is not done, then speculative explanations become merely mythological.

"This is precisely the way religion sets about explaining the world. Thunder and lightning are caused by deities. The world exists because it was created by a god. Disaster is the will of an omnipotent deity, or the triumph of an evil deity over an omnipotent deity. We die because we sinned long ago. Moreover, religion naïvely supposes that the fact that there is thunder and lightning, that the world exists, that disaster occurs in it, and that we die, is a proof that deities exist, that God created the world, and that we sinned long ago."[1] It is, however, no proof of such a hypothesis to point to the phenomena, since the explanation has been invented to cover these very facts.

If this procedure is followed, for any group of facts an indefinite number of myths can be advanced as explanations, and if there is no method of disverification or verification there can be no way of settling which is to be accepted. The result is the endless proliferation of incompatible speculative theories, from which we may choose whichever appeals to us, or, alarmed at the variability and uncertainty of private judgment, we may fly to the authority of the Church and accept the explanation accredited by revelation.

Guessing or Testing?

Because of the rigor of its method scientific thinking escapes this dilemma. Science is intolerant in the sense that one scientific hypothesis drives out another. Lavoisier's theory of oxygen and its action in combustion kills stone dead the theory of phlogiston, Harvey's theory of the circulation of the blood drives out Galen's, Galileo's law of motion overturns the Aristotelian theory that all motion depends on the operation of a mover.

The more likely hypothesis will also be of the greater value in prediction and for the control of the physical world; and

[1] Christopher Caudwell, *Studies in a Dying Culture.*

in its use it will call for revision and improvement on the basis of the results obtained. "If, of two hypotheses one exhibits more comprehensively and less symbolically the structure of the determinism of the phenomena it explains and their relation to the already established structure of reality, that hypothesis will be more powerful as an instrument for predicting the recurrence of such phenomena in real life."[1]

Hence the importance of the crucial test, which decides between one hypothesis and another. For example, the crucial tests of the Einstein theory, as compared with the Newtonian, were the bending of light, the perturbation of planetary orbits, the increase of mass of alpha particles and the shifts of the spectra of receding stars.

The editor of *The Humanist* discussing a recent theory says: "I suppose that one scientific guess is as good as another, and there is a touch of poetry in this conception which appeals to me." This is simply to abandon rational thinking. If one scientific guess is as good as another it is not scientific.

What is a Scientific Law?

Scientific thinking which failed to use the imagination to frame hypotheses could neither arrive at any comprehensive scientific theory nor could it have anything to say on the wider problems of human existence. Clearly this would be a strong inducement to remedy its deficiencies by seeking for some other method of finding such essential truths.

Unfortunately there are scientists who themselves reduce science to mere summaries of observed data, but this is a totally inadequate account of scientific law. A scientific law is *not* a bare summary of the facts. It goes beyond the evidence in order to explain it. It *interprets* the results of observation. Man would never have *mastered* his environment if he had not ventured beyond the facts to the system of truth which explains them. Merely to collect and summarise facts is hardly thinking at all. Scientific thinking is high-grade, energetic thinking. "Man," says Collingwood, "is the only animal who

[1] Christopher Caudwell, *Studies in a Dying Culture.*

thinks so hard that he transforms the whole structure of his life by its means. Everything human is due to man's power of thinking hard."[1] Scientific thinking means not taking things as they come, but asking questions, and asking questions cunningly and persistently, until we break through the confusing web of experience to the truth behind.

True knowledge is never the simple apprehension of things, either separately or in statistical aggregates. Inference is all. What matters is the secret behind the baffling evidence.

It would be a very poor detective story which *stopped* with the facts and not only offered no solution but was satisfied to present these facts as sufficient in themselves—there being no explanation at all to unify them, interpret them, make a story to explain them.

Now science is wholly concerned to discover the explanatory story, and that is what really matters. Of course, as in a detective story, fidelity to the facts is essential and no solution would be acceptable that did not take into account and deal convincingly with all the data with which we are presented.

Explanation lies beyond the Observed Facts

The very essence of scientific discovery is the explanation of the directly observed by what is not directly observed; the discovery of facts not available to direct observation by inference from observation, and the practical testing and verification of such inferences. Thus science passes beyond the empirical data to discover such facts as the rotation of the earth, the existence of atomic nuclei, cosmic radiation, radio stars.

The empiricism which stops short of inference is based upon the grandest foundation a philosophy can have, namely human stupidity, a philosophy which paralyses the ability to think by destroying the structuralised picture of the world. There is not a great scientist anywhere in the world who has not achieved his life's work by *overcoming* the facts. The paradox of scientific thought is that it must do two apparently opposite things at

[1] Collingwood, *Metaphysics*.

once—it must be strictly faithful to the facts (and that is the great lesson which empiricism has taught us), but it must never remain content with them. Science begins when the illusions of sense experience are transcended—when we see that the earth revolves on its axis and it is *not* the sun which moves. This was well put by Leonardo da Vinci when he said: "Nature is full of infinite reasons, which were never in experience,"[1] and splendidly asserted by Galileo when he described the aim of scientific investigation thus: "Against appearances, in which all agree, we make headway with reason." The great obstacle to science is common sense, the obvious, what men think "stands to reason." Scientists will break any law of thought to make a law of nature. Every advance in medicine, in physics, in chemistry, in biology, has been shocking, paradoxical, difficult to comprehend, a matter of picking up the stick by the other end.

Let us take a couple of simple examples; the discovery of oxygen and of the circulation of the blood. The commonsense view was that when anything burned it released something in it which streamed out in the form of flame—this they called *phlogiston*. The whole view was based upon one of those fundamental conclusions of common-sense observation which can set the whole of men's thinking on the wrong track for thousands of years. It answered to certain *prima facie* appearances, but in fact it was the exact opposite of the truth. It took Lavoisier to startle the world with the view that, when a thing burned, a gas in the air was combining with it to increase the weight of the oxidised material.

This was no mere summary of the observed data or statistical abstract of a number of measurements, it was a disconcerting hypothesis.

Harvey's theory of the circulation of the blood also seemed to run counter to common sense and ordinary observation. We may *know* (now) that the blood circulates round the body, but we certainly do not see it doing so. For centuries men saw the facts otherwise. Physiology and medicine, which is

[1] Leonardo, *Frammenti*, etc.

dependent upon it, are entirely a matter of explanatory theory which is itself taken to be *fact*, inferred fact, invisible fact, *behind* the observed data, inferred but so dependable as to be the basis of medical treatment and surgical operations.

An admirable example of the objectivity of both cell structure on the one hand, and the electro-physical realities behind radiation on the other, is to be seen in X-ray treatment for cancer, a method of treatment based on the fact that radiation has a destructive effect on the chromosomes of *dividing* cells. Hence its effect is particularly damaging to the endlessly proliferating cells of cancer.

To read through any issue of *Nature* would be convincing evidence of the fact that scientific knowledge, while based on facts, transcends them and is concerned with the ordered structural world of conceptual inference and not merely with the data.

It is amazing that not only philosophers, who often know very little science, but also scientists themselves in certain cases (Professor H. Dingle and Professor M. Polanyi are cases in point), can persuade themselves of a philosophy of science which is in flat contradiction to everything the working scientist believes.

How Science Advances

(1) That view of science which conceives it as no more than the cataloguing of observed data misses the important fact that advance in science springs from a new formulation which bears the marks of a deeper penetration of reality, which integrates existing facts more completely with the total structure, which survives more rigorous tests and gives a wider measure of control. Merely to summarise facts is not to state the whole truth, is not the way to understand the natural order, and gravely hinders the advance of science.

(2) Further, the endeavour of science is to search for relations between apparently disconnected things and "to correlate, and to equate our particular phenomena with more and more of the physical phenomena around and so to weave

a web of connection and interdependence."[1] Only thus do we come to understand the real structure of the world and to discover its laws. This takes us a long way from the mere ordering and cataloguing of observed facts.

(3) We must not underestimate the great contribution of the empiricists to scientific thought. Science is the concrete but intelligent apprehension of particular fact, i.e. of nature itself as it observably exists. From this dependence of all knowledge on immediate sensory experience science can never turn back. But both science and philosophy know to-day that there is no elusive thing-in-itself, existing independently of everything else and possessing its properties out of any relationship with other things and with the whole of which it is a part. This is what Whitehead calls "the fallacy of misplaced concreteness." For these isolated entities are *abstractions*. That is to say they do not, as is supposed, exist at all in this atomistic form. It is only by an isolation and separation imposed on the facts, tearing them out of the web of concrete existence, that they are seen as "bare facts". The fact has been *abstracted* from its environment. It is therefore in that form simply a mental construct—an *abstraction*. Reality does not consist of isolated facts.

[1] D'Arcy Wentworth Thompson, *On Growth and Form.*

CHAPTER THREE

THE SCEPTICAL PHILOSOPHER

The Limits of Human Reason

THE "hard facts" school, from the days of Hume to the present day, has rendered a valuable service not only to philosophy but to all human thinking. A great amount of baseless speculation and earnest metaphysical wrangling has been shown to be futile and misdirected.

We now see that to reach valid conclusions reason must never regard itself as an independent source of knowledge, as though by pure thought one could arrive at truths about the meaning of life, the nature of the world, or the existence of God; or build a whole philosophical system from premises whose truth is intuitively certain. Reason can only proceed on the basis of observed facts and what can be legitimately deduced from them.

It would appear indeed that the human understanding is strictly limited. Firstly, says the "hard facts" school, it is limited to statements of fact, which are simply so, there being no reason why they should be as they are and not otherwise. These facts are logically independent of each other, are given in experience, and can be verified by observation. Secondly, we may be certain of the truth of the propositions of logic and pure mathematics. These are purely abstract and formal, like an equation in algebra, and they make no assertion at all about the world of fact. If I say "It must be true that men are either bipeds or not," this provides no information whatsoever about the anatomy of men. It is not a statement about matters of fact and adds nothing to our knowledge. As Bertrand Russell said about mathematics, it "is a science in which we

c

never know what we are speaking of, or whether what we say is true"—true, that is to say, not as a logical implication but as referring to concrete fact—(of which it might or might not be true). Logical and mathematical "truths,"[1] therefore, cannot tell us anything about the world that we did not know before. If I make a statement, and then show that another statement is implied in it or deducible from it and other related statements, then I am not really going beyond my initial propositions. If *all men are mortal*, and if *Socrates is a man*, then it follows that *Socrates is mortal*. Logical processes and mathematical operations give us such *truths*, but these are neither new *facts* about the world, nor meaningful propositions which reveal the ultimate nature of a reality beyond direct experience; they merely reveal the implications of our assertions.

This sweeps aside a great mass of popular beliefs on the one hand and pretentious philosophising on the other. The sceptical philosopher is inclined to say with Hume: "The vast majority of human opinions are, and always have been worthless and devoid of reality. . . . Reasoning, however shrewd and persistent, directed upon the feeble and fallacious products of the imagination, is reasoning wasted, and all the edifices of thought erected upon no firmer basis than this are subjective shiftings, mischievous superstitions, pseudo-sciences, houses built of cards."

No Coherent World View

The full consequences of this position are not always realised. Professing a hard-headed acceptance of nothing beyond plainly verifiable data (apart from tautologies) a philosopher like Bertrand Russell finds himself faced with nothing but an inchoate, unorganised welter of facts—a multiverse rather than a universe. "The most fundamental of my intellectual beliefs," he says, "is that the idea that the world is a unity is rubbish. I think the universe is all spots and jumps, without

---

[1] Which some philosophers like to describe as *tautologies*, that is to say repetition of the same meaning in different words.

unity and without continuity, without coherence or orderliness, or any of the other properties that governesses love."[1]

Thus any coherent world view of any sort is rejected. All such interpretations of life, whether religious, or humanist, or ethical, or socialist, are "out."

On many occasions both in his writings and in broadcasting, one of the ablest and most typical of our contemporary sceptics, Professor A. J. Ayer, has made this abundantly clear. It is not the business of philosophy, he argues, to give us a philosophy of life. All that it can do is to criticise rash speculations, and make certain that we say what we mean and mean what we say. Its business is to clarify thought, not to express truths. He emphatically repudiates the responsibility of offering any guidance as to the conduct of life. "Questions of belief—questions of a religious, moral, political or generally 'cosmic' variety—are seldom if at all directly dealt with in contemporary philosophy. . . . Philosophy has nothing to do with questions of that kind." It is a highly professional occupation "which its practitioner should be left to practice," and as regards world views, "the contemporary philosopher's eye is characteristically cold, and his pen is apt to be employed as an instrument of deflation."[2]

This does not mean that Ayer and his friends have no beliefs, but they are not provided by philosophy and they are not sanctioned by philosophy. All that philosophy can do about our beliefs is to see that we do not overstep the limits of rationality in discussing them, or by seeking to prove them.

Philosophy in Retreat

Many modern philosophers go so far as to refuse to discuss such problems as the conflict between materialism and idealism, which they hold to be meaningless; nor will they consider *the mind—body problem*—whether there is a living soul connected with the material body.

Professor Ayer makes this quite clear. In his *Language, Truth*

[1] Quoted in Schlipp's *Library of Living Philosophers: Bertrand Russell.*
[2] G. J. Warnock, *English Philosophy since 1900.*

and Logic he says: "The problems with which philosophers have vexed themselves in the past, concerning the possibility of bridging the 'gulf' between mind and matter in knowledge or action, are all fictitious problems arising out of the senseless metaphysical conception of mind and matter, of minds and material things as substances."

The propositions of philosophy, he says, are not factual, but linguistic. Philosophy is a department of logic. There is therefore nothing in the nature of philosophy to warrant the existence of conflicting philosophical parties, such as *idealists* who reduce all material things to mind, and *materialists*, who accept the full reality of the material world and treat thought not as a substance, but as a function of brains.

Some philosophers, as we have already seen, may even go so far as to reject all scientific statements that pass beyond mere summaries of observations; or if they accept them at all, it is only as useful fictions and not as truths.

This scientific scepticism is the necessary conclusion of a purely empirical position. But if truth is limited to facts of observation and mere summaries of these, we certainly cannot arrive at the basic theories of modern science or even at genuine explanatory laws. From a finite number of observations no general proposition can be inferred. As Whitehead says, on these assumptions, "we must not ascribe, we must not expect, one step beyond our direct knowledge. The Positivist has no foothold on which he can rely for speculation beyond the region of direct observation. . . . There is no probability as to the future."[1] It follows that anything resembling a natural law is wholly unverifiable; and if, as is the case with some of these empiricists, the ultimate *facts* turn out to be our own sensations, then it is mere waste of time even to play with the idea that the general laws of any science could be solidly established upon these vanishing foundations.

The End of the Philosophic Quest

Philosophers have not always been so modest as to reject all

[1] Whitehead, *Adventures of Ideas*.

philosophising that passes beyond the province of pure logic. Bertrand Russell himself, for all his philosophical scepticism, has always held very definite views about human life and conduct, and has advocated these persuasively. The earlier empiricists, too, were men of faith. They opposed credulity, because reason alone led to the truth on which they believed life and society should be based. Locke, Hume, Voltaire, Bentham and Mill were men of affairs with plenty to say about the conduct of life. It is only in our time that the full implications of their position has been realised. The earlier empiricists, while vigorously rejecting superstition and metaphysics, simply accepted, without question, the highest ethical standards of their day and, in the Victorian Age, the optimistic hopes of that period for the future of mankind. They did not realise that views of this sort cannot be substantiated on the basis of the empirical philosophy they were advocating.

In our day this has been clearly recognised and this philosophy is now completely divorced from discussions as to what is good and what is evil, from theories as to the world and human life, from all those beliefs on which, ever since men became capable of rational enquiry, their actions have depended. The age-long search for the living truth on which our hope depends is finished. One finds *nothing*; and the search is ended.

Mind at the End of its Tether

The conclusion of this philosophy is simply *nihilism*, a darkening of inner enlightenment, an incapacity to go beyond the negation of faith. Thus an increasing number of people have no central point around which their beliefs and habits can be focused, and to which their endeavours can be related. They are increasingly at a loss to find a meaning in life and lack clear standards by which to weigh one line of conduct against another.

Society suffers when its members thus lose their vision of life, because with that loss they also lose what is most human in their common outlook and purpose, so that their life degenerates and disintegrates. As the *Times Literary Supplement* warns us: "We cannot be indifferent to the terrifying degree to which our society, on the surface still working so smoothly, has become a society almost utterly uncertain what its basic assumptions about the purpose and significance of human life are."[1]

The silence of philosophy is not to be considered solely in relation to the general question of whether it is possible to frame a theory of human existence, but in relation to the gathering clouds of perplexity and the growing urgency of the need for enlightenment in a period of world upheaval. Under these circumstances it can but lead to an increasing area of subjective disruption, the split personality, rational in its special field, open to irrationality in other departments.

The Age of Anxiety

Thus the air of elegant scepticism which was worn so gracefully in the 1920s and the early 1930s has vanished. In its place is an extreme malaise—so that if it has become fashionable to speak of the present as "the age of anxiety"—that malaise offers a sense in which the catch phrase is real.

Scepticism, then, has not stopped with the overthrow of superstition, religion and metaphysics. It has pushed criticism so far that when the plain man brings his problems to philosophy he is met with something like derision for expecting the professional thinkers to have any answers to his problems. But parallel to the scepticism of the professionals, though no doubt dependent upon it, the last half-century has witnessed, among an increasing number of thoughtful people, the steady erosion of all those conventional principles which nineteenth-century rationalism regarded as quite independent of the religious and speculative systems they abandoned. Dostoievsky declared that if God were dead "everything is permitted", Nietzsche, even more violently, called for a "transvaluation of all values" and derided the Christian ethic as a slave morality.

[1] *Times Literary Supplement*, February 1st, 1957.

Sartre in our day declares that since there are no absolute values and no providential purpose to guide him, man has the awful responsibility of making his own values and arbitrarily choosing his own destiny. Russell, somewhat melodramatically, but with a keen perception of the entire absence of a divine guarantee for the fulfilment of human hopes, tells us that "only within the scaffolding of these truths, only on the firm foundation of unyielding despair, can the soul's habitation henceforth be safely built."[1]

Philosophy in the Doldrums

It is hardly surprising that, since philosophers now keep as far away as possible from human problems, philosophy has become so neglected that the name of philosopher hardly signifies anything outside the universities. The exclusive property of semi-recluse institutions, it has grown widely apart from the everyday world of practical affairs—a professional speciality, no longer of general significance and interest.

We may hope that the ability and energy displayed in this kind of philosophising will be maintained and increased, because in that way its essential hollowness will at length be revealed in the reduction of thought and language to impalpable particles of logical dust.

Superstition Returns by the Back Door

It is not sufficient, however, to expose the pretensions of mysticism and metaphysics and then take refuge in silence. When, in the biblical parable, the unclean spirit was driven away, seeking rest and finding it not, he returned to the house whence he came and found it swept and garnished. "Then goeth he and taketh with himself seven other spirits more evil than himself and they enter in and dwell there; and the last state of that man becometh worse than the first."

And so the nihilism of modern philosophy encourages the very credulity and irrationalism it sets out to destroy. As

[1] Bertrand Russell, *Mysticism and Logic*.

Collingwood says in his criticism of Oxford philosophy, when students were informed that their teachers had no intention of giving them ideals to live for and principles to live by, the only inference they could draw "was that for guidance in the problems of life, since one must not seek it from thinkers or from thinking, from ideals or from principles, one must look to people who were not thinkers (but fools), to processes that were not thinking (but passion), to aims that were not ideals (but caprices), and to rules that were not principles (but rules of expediency). If these philosophers had wanted to train up a generation of Englishmen expressly as the potential dupes of every adventurer in morals or politics, commerce or religion, who should appeal to their emotions and promise them private gains which he could neither procure them nor even meant to procure them, no better way of doing it could have been discovered."[1]

Thus an extreme form of scepticism has exactly the opposite effect to that intended. When philosophy falls silent people do not cease asking what life is about, they seek for other paths to truth, which are not philosophical. They are driven to accept the view that there must be some faculty which can penetrate the veil of sense and apprehend spiritual reality directly. We are in a vicious circle and come round again to bogus metaphysics and transcendental visions.

We cannot be content that the situation should thus remain in permanent confusion. Philosophy itself has, in some quarters already begun to realise that the reaction against metaphysics has gone too far, that it wanted pruning and refining rather than removing by a surgical operation. Professor Ayer is now disposed to admit that there may be philosophical propositions; but the aim of philosophy remains, as far as he is concerned, to solve puzzles, verbal puzzles, not to discover truths. Some of his colleagues are prepared to go a little farther and allow us to construct imaginative world views, since it does not seem possible to do without them, but only if we realise that they are more of the nature of poetry than

[1] R. G. Collingwood, *An Autobiography*.

objectively true. Since no justification for believing them can be produced other than their utility, the most that this version of philosophy can offer us is an illusion to buck us up in the battle of life. We do not really believe; we merely believe that we have the right to believe that we might be right if we believed!

The Way Out

On what other grounds than this desperate desire to believe can we escape from a scepticism which leaves the world entirely empty of significance;

> From thought a crawling ruin
> From life a leaping mire,
> From a broken heart in the breast of the world,
> And the end of the world's desire?

We must realise that reason has a function beyond refuting error and condemning credulity, namely, that of seeking for scientific explanations beyond the bare data of observation, and for understanding of the meaning and significance of human life.

Scepticism denies *both* possibilities, and at first sight this strict limitation of the scope of human knowledge may seem splendidly scientific—the expression of a tough, realistic attitude with no nonsense about it. But it is not scientific. Science begins when we pass from empirical data to unifying and explanatory laws and theories.

It is equally unscientific to abandon the attempt to explain human existence; and the same method of constructive thinking which establishes the wide embracing theories of science is at our disposal for the essential task of constructing a philosophy of life and human history.

CHAPTER FOUR

SCIENCE IN THE MAKING

Philosophy and Common Sense

AS long ago as 1925 G. E. Moore of Cambridge published an article called "A Defence of Common Sense" in which he sharply criticised those philosophers who denied such obvious truths as the existence of the external world or of other minds and the reality of time. Moore pointed out that these very philosophers knew these things to be true even though they questioned them. He declared that philosophy of this sort was obviously absurd, but proceeded to raise a further question of considerable interest, namely, what exactly is *meant* by such perfectly true statements as "the external world exists", or "this table exists".

More recently Professor Ayer, a leading protagonist of the new school of philosophy has, in somewhat similar terms, sounded a strategic retreat from the sceptical attitude towards science implied in logical positivism.

It was, of course, really absurd to go on declaring that science is restricted to sense data and statistical summaries when manifestly in every department it was establishing theories and discovering realities far beyond the level of observable data. When philosophy contradicts experience to this extent, we do not abandon common sense, we revise our philosophy.

Ayer points out that since the results of scientific investigation and much everyday inference are assured, it is unnecessary to seek a justification of their methods by pure logic. Rather we have to reverse the process and see what methods are actually followed in finding what is certainly the truth.

To ask for a formal or logical guarantee of the validity of the process which results in what all accept as true and which is consistently verified in practice is to raise a purely fictitious problem.

The Method of Science

What are these methods of reasoning? It is clear that there is no *logical* derivation of scientific conclusions from the observed data. The Newtonian theory is not and could not be an induction from accumulated data. The theory of evolution is not the result of a purely logical process working up from the observed biological facts. Scientific theories are *hypotheses*, tested and verified by subsequent observation or experiment.

As Kant showed long ago, scientific theory cannot be distilled from the data in a mechanical way. It can only come from an attempt to *understand* the data. The truth *depends* on the data, but it is *discovered by* our intellects, by the creative and ordering activities of the mind. We are not passive observers waiting until it pleases nature to reveal her secrets. We must question her and we must ourselves construct explanatory theories to interpret the facts before us.

It is the method of hypothesis tested by experiment which delivers us from the prison of immediate experience and allows us legitimate inference to laws and truths beyond these observed data.

But if there is a valid procedure which discovers broad generalisations, comprehensive laws and far-reaching theories in the field of science, may it not be that we have in our hand a method which we can use in those fields which deal with human behaviour and social development? Naturally, in extending the scientific method to the humanistic field necessary modifications of the method to its subject matter must be made, but this will not mean supplementing scientific explanation by supernatural or vitalistic factors, but on the contrary, the same rigid exclusion of such extraneous causes which has brought success to the scientific method in other departments.

The Place of Imagination in Scientific Reasoning

The method of hypothesis involves three stages—the accumulation of all the available facts; a guess or intuitive leap to a possible explanation based on analogical reasoning; and finally the testing of the hypothesis.

This is an over-simplification, because even the collection of the facts requires some preliminary theory, so that facts and theory are always dialectically connected. "How odd," says Darwin, "that anyone should not see that all observation must be for or against some view if it is to be of any service. . . . There must be a view preceding observation, that is, a theory or hypothesis which lends value to the fact finding. No one could be a good observer unless he was an active theoriser."[1]

The whole process is admirably demonstrated by Darwin's discovery of the origin of species. It was, he says, on the voyage of the *Beagle* that he became convinced of the mutability of species. The *possibility* that evolution occurs in nature must have been known to him before, but it was his observations during the voyage of the changes in structure correlated with changes of climate and the physical environment that convinced him that evolution is a *fact*. In his *Autobiography* Darwin states that before the publication of *The Origin of Species* he never came across a single naturalist who doubted the permanence of species, in spite of the work of Lamarck some forty years earlier.

Darwin then began an immense collection of relevant facts which continued until 1842, when he drafted the first part of his theory. During this time he realised that selection by breeders of horses, pigeons, dogs, etc., accounts for the great variety of these animals, but failed to see how selection could be applied to organisms living in a state of nature. Then in 1838, after reading Malthus on *Population*, a book which stated that the population tended to increase faster than the food supply, he transferred Malthus' theory, *by analogy*, to nature and advanced the hypothesis that in the struggle for

[1] Charles Darwin, *Autobiography*.

existence favourable variations would tend to be preserved, and unfavourable ones to be destroyed. Thus nature would do the selecting and the result would be the formation of a new species.

This was one half of the theory. But he was still puzzled as to why animals descended from the stock *diverge* into so many different types. The answer came to him in a sudden flash of intuition while driving in his carriage. It was that they become adapted to their special environments. "The modified offspring of all dominant and increasing forms tend to become adapted to many and highly developed places in the economy of nature."

The theory was now complete and was first published as a paper in 1858. *The Origin of Species* appeared in the following year.

We thus see the important part that analogy plays in suggesting new hypotheses. Darwin first recognised the resemblance of the variations of species in nature to the more familiar variations which are selected by animal breeders, and then he perceived the analogy between this artificial selection and the competition for the means of subsistence in nature. It is the mark of genius to perceive such similarities.

It must always be remembered that analogy is not proof, it is only a suggestion. The resemblances may not be fundamental at all, in which case nothing could be more fallacious. What is suggested by the analogy must be tested by the facts.

Darwin is emphatic that "An unverified hypothesis is of little or no value." In the course of his life he investigated a great many subjects from barnacles and earthworms to orchids and coral reefs. He formed innumerable hypotheses, the product of "his richness of imagination". His son says that "it was as though he were charged with theorising power ready to flow into any channel, so that no fact, however small, could avoid releasing a stream of theory." But on the other hand his scientific integrity led him always to seek to refute these very hypotheses. No sooner had he thought of his theory of evolution than he opened a note-book in which he recorded every published fact, new observation or thought that occurred to him, which was *opposed* to his discovery. "Thus the richness of ideas and speculative power of his mind was balanced by his power of judging and condemning the thoughts that occurred to him."[1]

The first step after the collection of the facts is a guess or intuitive leap, an act of the imagination—thus the hypothesis is framed. There follows the severe testing of hypothesis by experiment and observation. Scientists are insistent that their work involves the formulation and rejection of very many hypotheses before one is found which stands up to verification. This is where science is sharply distinguished from the myth-making type of explanation which may be content with any theory which links the facts together in a coherent manner, and on the other hand from the theory of "useful fictions" which is content with any theory that "works". The scientific theory has to run the gauntlet of crucial tests to see whether it is more than a plausible story which makes sense of the facts, or more than a convenient instrument for practical use.

The Method of Disverification

No hypothesis may be entertained in science unless it is possible to recognise the state of affairs which would prove it, *and the state of affairs which would disprove it*. If a belief is so conceived that it is compatible with no matter what facts of observation, then it should not be entertained. Animistic, theological and metaphysical theories are often so conceived that they are immune against tests of any sort; but only where the facts of direct observation and experience can either lend evidential support or disprove a theory are we thinking rationally.

The strength and validity of scientific theories depends on the peculiar severity of this testing process. It is not merely a matter of conducting experiments which *confirm* the theory. The theory must be tested by trying in every conceivable way to *refute it*. Merely to be able to use or apply a hypothesis does

[1] Charles Darwin, *Autobiography*. (Notes by Francis Darwin.)

not test it, does not confirm it. It *could* be useful even if false. Many such theories have served the purpose of science. The idea of heat as a sort of fluid, a delicate material substance, the small particles of which have an attraction to materials but a natural tendency to fly apart from one another, and many erroneous theories of light, of electricity, of combustion, served for years before they were discarded because they were *false*, rather than because they were *useless*. It is by searching for refutations that we establish scientific truths. To the extent to which we fail in these attempts an increasing degree of probability attaches itself to the theory.

The Method of Verification

The positive process of verification, is to deduce from the theory what should necessarily follow and then conduct observations or experiments to see whether it does follow.

Maxwell in 1866 advanced the hypothesis that light-waves were electro-magnetic waves—perhaps the greatest physical discovery of the nineteenth century. Experimental confirmation was not forthcoming for twenty years. It was in 1886 that Herz, in a remarkable series of experiments, obtained full confirmation of Maxwell's theory.

In 1846 Adams at Cambridge and Leverrier in France became convinced that the motions of the planet Uranus were only to be accounted for as the effects of a planet which had never been seen. Working by the Newtonian theory they predicted its magnitude, motion and position. Acting on their theory, a German astronomer focused his telescope on the spot and the new planet was seen. It was named Neptune (and not Newton, it being one of the strange ways of astronomers to keep to the names of Gods in whom they have no belief).

Does Science Understand Reality?

Science is quite convinced that in framing such hypotheses it is passing beyond the observed facts to understand the world. What it discovers transcends sense experience but is none the less part of the physical world-order and determines what happens at the level of sense experience; hence the possibility of verification by prediction and experiment. Science, therefore, is by no means content with observable data, but by means of explanatory theories immeasurably extends the realms of human knowledge. Thus the use of the microscope, and of delicate instruments to detect radiation, or of tracer atoms showing the movement of matter within living bodies, are constantly revealing new worlds behind our everyday experience.

Theories are genuine conjectures, highly informative guesses about the world, *which are capable of being tested*. They are not plausible fictions but serious attempts to discover the truth.

The claim of scientific theory to reveal the actual condition of the natural world is crucial. If a theory is capable of disproof then it can clash with reality and, when it does, we know that there *is* a reality, that there is something to remind us that our ideas may be mistaken.

Science Fiction

Science fiction does not only consist of scientific romances; there is a well-known positivist or pragmatist theory of science, to which we have already alluded, which regards all such entities as atoms, molecules, electrons and so on as fictions or mental constructs which are not to be taken as actually existing. Similarly, scientific theories are regarded as purely instrumental, that is to say as convenient ways of arranging data in a systematic form, but not as giving us the truth about objective reality.

The theory of the "ether" extending through space and providing a medium for the transmission of light and other forms of radiation was attractive and convenient as a theory, but was it true? A great variety of theories about the ether were worked out by mathematicians, and scientists like Kelvin firmly believed in its existence. Experiments subsequently demonstrated that no such substance existed, among them the famous Michelson-Morley experiment of 1881. The theory was further refuted by astronomical observations of great weight and accuracy. The death blow to all such mechanistic theories of the ether was finally given by Maxwell's electromagnetic theory of light. Desperate endeavours were made to give the ether mechanical properties that would be compatible with Maxwell's equations, and "ethers" of an altogether incredible complexity arose in obedience to this demand; none were successful and the attempt to explain the transmission of light and other forms of radiation by these mechanical models was abandoned.

The scientist thus distinguishes between useful conceptions and truth. He pushes his tests beyond considerations of mere convenience. He wants to know whether his theories are *true*. Where a theoretical formulation is only a matter of conveniently ordering the data, we have what has been described as a computation rule, and there is no need to go on testing this because it is not supposed to be true. We can go on using such a rule as long as it remains useful, but we make no further claims for it.

The view that atoms are "fictions" was advanced by Mach, Poincaré, Ostwald and others; but Ostwald in 1909 abandoned it, having become convinced that "we have now become possessed of experimental evidence" of the atomic nature of matter, and that even "the most cautious science was justified in now speaking of the experimental proof of the atomic theory of matter".[1] The theory is less credible when it is realised that it not only rejects atomic theories, but logically should reject the rotation of the earth, the Copernican astronomy, the circulation of the blood, and many other well established theories that we now take as facts.

The fictional approach to scientific theory is by no means new.

Cardinal Bellarmine tried to persuade Galileo to describe the planetary theory as no more than an instrument of calculation, and not a description of the actual universe. Galileo refused and was brought before the Inquisition.

[1] W. Ostwald, *Grundriss der allegemeinen Chemie.*

Berkeley was alarmed at Newton's theories, which seemed to him to lead to a decline in religious faith since they were a proof of the power of the human intellect unaided by divine revelation to uncover the secrets of our world. He therefore wished the theory to be regarded as a convenient instrument for the calculation and prediction of phenomena (or appearances), but not a true description of astronomical fact.

This view, which has its advocates to-day, holds that there are two kinds of knowledge: the one, *scientific*, which does not claim to discover the real, but merely forges practical instruments of prediction; the other, *ontological*, which unveils the essential nature of reality. The scientist may be allowed all the scope he likes provided that he confines himself to a purely *instrumental* attitude to his theories. This raises philosophy, religion and revelation to a different and higher level of truth, since they alone can give us information as to the ultimate nature of reality.

The fictional theory of the nature of science is content with the surface of things, finding reality in the everyday world of appearances which has surface but no depth. The world actually is just what it appears to be; only scientific theories are not what they appear to be, neither explaining nor describing the world, but only facilitating its manipulation.

Yet many people, including some scientists who are mainly concerned with the practical applications of their work, cheerfully accept this view, quite oblivious of its philosophical implications and of the fact that they have broken with the Galilean tradition of asserting the *reality* of the entities they have discovered and have fallen into the arms of Cardinal Bellarmine and his like.

Science asserts its right to pass beyond appearances and observable phenomena, denying their finality and adequacy. The constructive thought of man, which interprets and changes the world, is never a mere register of observed data; indeed, its task is to overturn the surface truth in order to explain it, to reduce the chaos of brute facts to an order given by a deeper penetration of material reality.

Science and Sociology

We have established the fact that there is a valid scientific method. Can the same method be applied to man and society?

This has been denied. It is asserted that the methods of science are inadequate for this task and that recourse must be had to a higher faculty of spiritual apprehension. This alone, we are told, can reveal the moral standards and spiritual principles by which society must be ordered, and this alone can show us the ultimate purpose of human life.

The resort to transcendental truth is unnecessary and certain to lead to error and confusion.

There is no need to resort to such methods to discover the explanations and theories, the values and principles that are required to frame a philosophy of history.

It is our intention to show that we can clearly discriminate between legitimate and illegitimate theories which transcend the facts, so that the acceptance of a thorough-going scepticism in relation to mysticism in all its forms need not, as it has done in so many cases, involve us in a scepticism so complete as to limit us to the *physical* sciences, or even more radically to undermine science itself along with supernaturalism and the idealist philosophy.

The scientific method in philosophy rejects that speculative or intuitive metaphysics which is based on a privileged short cut to truth, habitually insensitive to the distinction between pictorial or emotional appeals and factual meaning, and it avoids those theories which under conditions of extreme tension, frustration or distress regress from the scientific to pre-scientific patterns of belief, theories which may be consoling but are certainly spurious.

The upshot of our thinking will therefore be something very much less comprehensive than the religious and metaphysical systems of the past; but we must make up our minds to accept not what we would like to be true but what can validly be established, not the blinding truth of a complete revelation or the assurance of a Providence making all things work together for good, but light enough to live by—and that is enough. And if we think it is not enough, at any rate it is all we are going to get. For the moment we begin to apply objective tests to our philosophies their whole nature changes. They cease to be "metaphysical" and become both more limited and more reliable. Perhaps they cease to be "philosophies" altogether.

This is a shattering "come down" for many people. It strips them of many high-sounding and pretentious but consoling transcendental truths. But on the other hand there is something bracing about the toughness, the down-to-earth quality of scientific thinking. And it escapes the awful peril which besets those whose balloons may at any moment be catastrophically deflated by the piercing arrows of rational criticism. Perhaps, too, it restores to philosophy, what has been missing since Hume, that sense of the ridiculous which saves one from taking seriously everything that is said solemnly.

Scientific Truth never Final or Complete

A scientific philosophy gives us the truth, but not the whole truth, not the final truth and not the truth about the whole. We have to be on our guard against extending the scope of a theory to include more than it can legitimately cover, or attributing to it a completeness and finality which can belong to no system devised by man.

We have two errors to guard against: On the one hand the danger of dogmatism, of believing that there is an all-sufficient, all-general principle, a single fundamental proposition that adequately explains everything; on the other hand, just because we cannot have complete certainty and exhaustive truth, despair of finding any truth at all.

The desire to know may be obscured by the desire to think we know. Some compelling theory presents itself and, by turning our attention away from objections to it, we may obtain the comfort of believing it, although, if we had resisted the wish for comfort, we should have come to see that the opinion was less than the whole truth by a very long way. There is no ultimate reality which removes all perplexity.

No theory can even pretend to tell us anything about the entire universe: cosmic philosophies are impossible. We cannot speculate beyond the range of experimental verification, and that is of necessity limited.

No theory is completely true; and the more useful it is, the more it is applied, the more quickly and thoroughly will it be revised and recast. The endless transformation of even the most impressive of human systems and scientific theories is a sobering fact.

The Sceptical Fallacy

Yet there is no reason in the relativity and imperfection of scientific theory for abandoning certainty. There is a very great difference between the certainty which is sufficient for us to stake even our lives on, and some absolute metaphysical certainty, which is what some people demand, and, of course, demand in vain. Philosophy should teach us to give ourselves with absolute seriousness and devotion to partial aims and relative truth. It must pronounce the inevitable incompleteness of all human truth, but it must simultaneously exhort us to serve with unrestricted devotion the truth that is ours.

In science we are constantly faced with new theories which render obsolete considerable areas of accepted knowledge; some, like evolution and relativity, revolutionise the whole of science, and there is always doubt and controversy on the fringes of knowledge. But the constant revision of scientific theory throws no doubt on the validity of science but rather enhances it.

Doubt is usually the prelude to fresh advance. The very lack of definiteness on such questions as the origin of life, or the nature of proteins and protoplasm, actually indicates the readjustments and fresh insights made necessary by the rapid *advance* in these fields. It is when we are penetrating more deeply and extending our knowledge that concepts become blurred and long established facts lose their certainty.

No scientist is the least perturbed at this, but philosophers who know no science are often filled with alarm. The scientist is aware that the permanent body of fully verified and acceptable fact is enormous and will not be overthrown by fresh discoveries. Relativity theory throws no doubt on the theory of gravity as it affects us, or the planets. New theories of biochemistry do not change the basic facts of physiology.

A theory does not have to be fool-proof. Consider medicine. It is based on a vast mass of ascertained fact and reliable theory, but it cannot be *applied* with mathematical certainty. Mistakes can be made and are made, even by the most experienced. There is still and must always be the need for estimating chances, probability, judgment, inspired guess work, both in diagnosis and treatment. Yet this is no reason for abandoning medicine and going back to the days before it was a science.

Revolution in Scientific Thought

Science does not develop by a smooth progress from imperfect to more perfect theories but by a series of revolutionary leaps. For centuries a scientific theory or even a complete theory of the universe—a cosmology—will hold its ground and be generally accepted as "natural", obvious and mere common sense. Then comes a period of disintegration and uncertainty, its adequacy is no longer unquestionable, finally some completely new theory is advanced, is at first bitterly resisted but at last is generally accepted. At such times the human mind passes through a revolutionary crisis, all its categories are changed, its whole frame of reference is transformed.

Among the larger shifts in the mental perspective one could mention the Copernican and Darwinian revolutions, which transformed the entire world picture; among the radical changes in particular sciences are the mechanistic theory of matter as formulated by Galileo, Descartes and Newton, the discovery of the circulation of the blood, the germ theory of disease, the electro-magnetic theory of matter, and many others.

It may well happen that a series of new theories may do

more than modify in certain particulars the older scientific picture, they may, taken together, revolutionise the entire cosmology. Consider the work of the seventeenth century. This shifted the centre of things and revealed the colossal possibilities of the age of science. It was part of the emergence of a new kind of Western civilisation, confident of its power to exist independently of the supernatural.

At any level these revolutions in thought are painful and difficult, but particularly so when their cumulative effects and the industrial and social changes that these ultimately give rise to, combine to change the whole world perspective. Then the demands of growing life lead us to think and do things quite inconsistent with existing conceptions and codes; the appeal of the whole system of ideas underlying these principles and categories is weakened and we begin to seek for a new system of ideas through which we may justify the new modes of behaviour.

Intellectual advance is thus more than a piecemeal modification of the existing pattern—it transforms the whole intellectual scene, loosens rigid and constricting moulds of thought, undermines existing categories. Old habits of thinking are unfrozen. Even the kind of question that people think important is changed. We are led step by step to change our angle of vision, to pass from one way of interrogating the world to another.

CHAPTER FIVE

THE MEANING OF HISTORY

(1) The Philosophers

CONTEMPORARY philosophy lends support, wittingly or unwittingly, not only to defeatist views of man but to theories of history which are for the most part sceptical, pessimistic or plainly reactionary. These theories must now be examined.

Toynbee has said that "a society cannot maintain its social cohesion unless a decisive majority of its members hold in common a number of guiding ideas and ideals."[1] This is true and yet it is widely recognised that the West has no generally accepted world view to-day. "World views are out", as our contemporary philosophers say.[2] It is equally well known that Marxism is a world outlook which has won the allegiance of millions. "Its abiding power in the present," says Professor Mackinnon, "is the sense of hope which it still gives to its devotees." At a moment when the emotional temper of the West is one of despair, the Marxist offers "a map that seems at once to take in the whole of historical reality and somehow to reveal the working of the system. It claims to be an explanation which will embrace all historical events, such as wars, revolutions, legislative changes—and all social institutions such as property, contractual relations and forms of government, in a single view."[3]

The chief ideological competitors of Marxism in the world

[1] A. Toynbee, *An Historian's Approach to Religion*.

[2] D. F. Pears, (Ed.) *The Nature of Metaphysics*.

[3] The Rev. Professor D. M. Mackinnon, *Christian Faith and Communist Faith*.

to-day fall into four main groups: The optimistic world philosophies, the pessimistic philosophies, the various forms of historical scepticism, and finally the retreat to traditionalism.

I. OPTIMISTIC WORLD PHILOSOPHIES

(1) *Positive Christianity*

There are many contradictory trends in the Christian tradition. One of these, as we shall attempt to show later, is other-worldly and profoundly pessimistic about this life. But from time to time there has appeared a more positive and optimistic Christian view of history. This, unlike Eastern mysticism and certain forms of Christianity, accepts the reality of time and the importance of history. It looks forward to the ultimate victory of social justice and the transformation of all human relationships into the Christian pattern. It believes that "God is working his purpose out as year succeeds to year" and that the Church is God's appointed and divinely guided instrument in achieving this.

This trend has found expression in the numerous "communist" sects which have flourished through the centuries, some of them very numerous and influential and against which the orthodox Church waged bloody crusades of extermination. These sects have denounced the rich and defended the poor, they have condemned the pomp and pride of ecclesiastics and not infrequently launched such revolutionary movements as the Peasants' Revolts of England and Germany and the Hussite Rebellion in Bohemia. In our day this tendency has expressed itself in various forms of Christian Socialism and Christian social action here, on the continent and in the United States.[1]

In spite of its belief in social justice and the redemption of society, we have in this movement an ideology which is based upon faith in a transcendent deity who guides the historical

---

[1] The immensely important role of this type of religion in the English Revolution of 1640, when it was the driving force of the Levellers and of Winstanley's Utopian communists, has been well brought out in Christopher Hill's *The English Revolution* and in Morton's *The English Utopia*.

process to its predestined end and watches over his servants. In a somewhat more philosophical form, this optimistic faith affirms its belief in "the moral order of the universe" which in the last resort brings evil to naught and ensures ultimate victory to the right.

(i) *What evidence is there for the existence of this benevolent deity?*

(*a*) The standard arguments for the existence of God have carried little conviction since the time of Kant, and even less since the general acceptance of evolutionary theory.

(*b*) What is left, and what is really the only convincing argument, is the claim that the religious hypothesis best fits the facts which demand explanation—in other words, it is an explanatory myth. Now, as we have seen, this is the most unsatisfactory type of hypothesis because in the realm of myths your guess is as good as mine and we can have as many different explanations as there are myth makers. What is needed is a crucial test based on the fact that there could be certain facts which would disprove it. As we have said earlier, if belief is so conceived that it is compatible with no matter what facts of observation, then this is the kind of hypothesis that cannot be entertained.

(*c*) That this is the case with the conception of Providence can be seen if we ask how it explains the evil in the world, which would seem inconsistent with a benevolent Deity. This may be done: (1) by denying the existence of evil, since all discord is "harmony not understood", and "all partial evil, universal good"; (2) by arguing that if we could understand God's purposes we should see that we are living in the best of all *possible* universes (not the best of *conceivable* universes); (3) or by trying to find consolation in misfortune— "poverty is good for the soul", "God takes away from us the child we have learned to love too much", "suffering strengthens character", and so on and so on.

Now on reflection we see that what this really means is that the theory of Providence is compatible with any kind of universe, good, bad or indifferent. No matter how much evil demonstrably exists, the theory is unimpaired. This would be like a scientific theory which was compatible with *all* experimental results and observations whatsoever!

(*d*) Suppose we modify the theory to allow man's free-will enough scope to frustrate God's intentions; in that case the doctrine of Providence is not much help, since evil men can go their own way and God's will is manifestly *not* done on earth as it is in Heaven.

(*e*) Suppose then that we change the conception of God to that of a being with a *limited* power for good; once again we have really abandoned the theory of Providence. Moreover it will be difficult to prove the existence of a supernatural force, not omnipotent and not of human origin, which comes to the assistance of the right. The only evidence would be that right sometimes wins, a fact which does not require belief in any sort of God to explain it. If right always won, that might suggest Providential aid—but then again it might just as well indicate that we can very well do without it.

(ii) This brings us to second form of optimistic world view which holds that there is a Moral Order in the universe which will ensure the ultimate victory of right. *What evidence is there of such a view?*

(*a*) If there is, now, such a moral order, what is evil doing within it? Is it perhaps an illusion, for if the world is in fact a moral order then whatever is is right?

(*b*) If it does not mean this, then it can only mean that there is a force not ourselves which makes for righteousness. Is this irresistible? If so, what happens to the freedom of the will? If the overriding of free-will does not matter, why could not Providence have made the world free from sin and kept it so?

(*c*) If, however, this Moral Force is not irresistible we are back at the notion of a limited God for which there can be no convincing evidence since evil frequently triumphs.

If good is ultimately to prevail it would seem to be more likely to do so the more we rely on ourselves and not on the Moral Order of the universe. *We* have got to make that moral order if ever it is to exist. It most certainly does not exist now.

(2) *The Christian Philosophy of History*

A number of theologians and historians have attempted to work out a Christian sociology and philosophy of history based on a critical examination of the existing social order in the light of Christian ethics. They anticipate the emergence of a distinct type of Christian civilisation which will supersede our present "pagan society".[1]

This philosophy looks back to a sort of golden age of corporate Christian living and economic justice in the middle ages which was overcome by the rise of capitalism and nationalism, and looks forward to the return of Christendom under the inspiration of a renewed and purified Church.

Historians regard this historical picture as mythological and philosophers are critical of its scholastic theology. Its idealisation of Catholic practice in the middle ages and its faith in the power of Christianity to create a just society would seem to be contradicted both by history and the plain fact that traditionally Catholic countries like Spain, Portugal and pre-war Poland have failed to develop a humanistic and liberal civilisation.

Nevertheless, Christian Sociology is highly critical of capitalism, attributing its evils to the break-up of corporate life at the time of the Reformation and the supplanting of the Christian social ethic by competitive individualism—"the negation of any system of thought or morals which can be described as Christian. Compromise is as impossible between the Church of Christ and the idolatry of wealth, which is the practical religion of capitalist societies, as it was between the Church and the State idolatry of the Roman Empire."[2]

The social ideal of Christianity as thus set forth has attracted many disturbed consciences within the Church, and in the face of an age which is rapidly losing its faith it does at least offer something. In such circumstances almost any positive

[1] Among those who have contributed to this movement one may mention Jacques Maritain, Christopher Dawson, Canon Demant and Barbara Ward.

[2] R. H. Tawney, *Religion and the Rise of Capitalism*.

creed, however far-fetched and over-simplified, is sure of a ready audience. It has a particularly strong appeal to those in revolt against the evils of an acquisitive society, and that appeal is all the stronger for some because it stops short of socialism.

This is just what is wanted by those who are serious enough to be critical of capitalism but not serious enough to face the necessity of socialism. It offers instead a return to medieval economic practices, resort to Divine Grace, the preaching of a utopian morality and a miscellaneous programme of partial reforms.

The great sincerity of many of its leaders in defending racial equality and attacking atomic war policies must be cordially recognised, but as a solution of the crisis of capitalism it can only have the effect of holding back many who are deeply critical of capitalism, diverting their idealism into harmless and futile channels. This, in the words of Marx, is only "so much worthless earnestness." He characterises movements of this sort as "half lamentation, half lampoon; half the echo of the past, half menace of the future; at times, by its bitter, witty and incisive criticism, striking the bourgeoisie to the very heart's core, but always ludicrous in its effect through total incapacity to comprehend the march of history."[1]

(3) *The Liberal Faith in Progress*

This is the third type of optimistic philosophy. It is the faith that "freedom slowly broadens down from precedent to precedent". Whether this theory is held in its original liberal form, or as is more generally the case to-day, as gradualist socialism, it has been sadly discredited by the failure of reason, morality and idealism to overcome the forces of evil and reaction in the world.

The difficulties of a reformist policy in an age of crisis are immense. It is confronted with the threat of social disaster unless class interests are challenged and a thoroughgoing socialist programme is put into operation. But should it attempt to do so it is confronted with the whole force of

[1] Marx, *The Communist Manifesto.*

monopoly capitalism, which maintains its power by every means, including violence, and has at its disposal the press, the radio, education, the law and a considerable range of ideo-logical weapons, backed by the Establishment. Thus advance is blocked, involving the working class in increasing sacrifices and the whole community ultimately in war and social collapse.

The perplexities and uncertainties which thus inevitably characterise liberalism and labourism are the themes of endless jibes at the collapse of their optimism. The cynical delight at human failure which is so frequently displayed, accompanied as it is by an air of superior wisdom and deeper spiritual perception, is one of the least pleasant attitudes of the bright young men of our day.

II. THE PESSIMISTIC PHILOSOPHIES OF HISTORY

(1) *Negative Christianity*

The failure of progressivism leads straight to the pessimistic conclusion that what always and necessarily thwarts human aspirations and endeavours is *original sin*, in the sense that man has a nature which sees and approves the better and follows the worse. "We may speculate and we may fail to understand why original sin exists. Of the fact that it does exist there can be no denial."[1] The theologians of the extreme right are well to the fore in stressing the total depravity of human nature and its social consequences.

There could hardly be a hypothesis more open to rational objection than this one. It is a typical example of explaining a phenomenon by giving it a name. Why do people behave badly? Because they have an ineradicable tendency to sin. How do you know that they have such a tendency? Because they habitually behave badly. This is no explanation at all.[2]

[1] *Times Literary Supplement*, Leading Article on Utopianism and Original Sin, February 7th, 1958.

[2] For a further discussion of this subject see Chapter 10, "The Fall of Man."

(2) *Decline and Fall*

"In our era an obsolete economy turns to the politics of barbarism and the culture of chaos," says Herbert Aptheker. In consequence history becomes senseless or is seen as a mysterious, cyclical, non-progressive drama of tragic significance. Spengler is one of those who have taken a cyclical view of history which interprets the present age as one of predestined decay. The signs are patent: the spread of socialism, the decay of religion, increasing dependence on the social services. Decline is inexorable. "Only dreamers believe that there is a way out. Optimism is cowardice."[1] Spengler regards intellectuality as an omen of decadence, and the ideal of a just society as sentimentality.

"Man is a beast of prey. I say it again and again. All the would-be moralists and social ethics people who claim or hope to be 'beyond all that' are only beasts of prey with their teeth broken, who hate others on account of the attacks which they themselves are wise enough to avoid."[2] "We finally have learned that which I shall openly tell you: the ability to hate. Whoever is not able to hate is not a man, and history is made by men."[3] *What* it is that we have to hate is plain enough. It was all that Hitler hated, for Spengler became his devoted supporter.

Spengler was profoundly influenced by Nietzsche, whose influence pervaded so much of pre-war and pre-fascist German thinking. Nietzsche longed for and anticipated the end of humanitarianism and the coming of a new aristocracy of power, with new values, the values of a master morality. "Socialism is the tyranny of the lowest and the stupidest carried to its extreme limits, the end-result of modern ideas and their latent anarchism. Christianity, Humanitarianism the French Revolution and Socialism are all the same thing."[4]

The decline of our corrupt civilisation, says Nietzsche, is bound to produce an age of pessimism and therefore of

[1] O. Spengler, *Man and Technics*.   [2] O. Spengler, *The Hour of Decision*.
[3] O. Spengler, *Politische Schrifte*.   [4] F. Nietzsche, *The Will to Power*.

nihilism. But there are two kinds of nihilism—the nihilism of spiritual decay and retrogression, and the nihilism springing from enhanced power of the spirit. "I exult in the progressive militarisation of Europe and in its inner anarchy," he says. "The days of sneaking hypocrisy are numbered."[1] A new type of man is appearing who will be the embodiment of the Will to Power.

The whole process of history has been an unending succession of experiments in the production of the superman. "After a long and costly sequence of virtue, fitness, industry, self-coercion and happy accidents there will appear at last a man, a monster of power who will demand a monster of a task. For it is our power that rules us."[2]

This is said to be the real meaning of the Eternal Recurrence which is the secret of history. "Know ye what the world is? A marvel of power without beginning, without end, power in solid, brazen majesty, bounded by nothing save its own bounds. Power everywhere, in the play of its forces and its will at once one and many, now piling up, now sinking down, a sea of tumultuous and torrential power, eternally changing, eternally returning, with immense cycles of recurrence, in the ebb and flow of its forms passing from the utmost simplicity into the utmost complexity. . . . Blessing itself as that which must eternally return, as a Becoming that knows no satiety, no weariness—a world of everlasting self-creation, of everlasting self-destruction, Beyond Good and Evil, without end or aim."[3]

Less hysterically nihilistic but equally pessimistic was Burckhardt, who poured scorn on those who made history the story of man's progress. "Optimists, mediocre fellows, and obstinate philistines. . . . A real philosophy of history ought to bear in mind what for ever *is* and never *develops*."[4] It cannot consist in constructing a picture of man's progress. It ought to be based on the realisation of the unchangeable nature of man, on the fundamental qualities of man, many bad, some

[1] F. Nietzsche, *The Will to Power.*
[2] F. Nietzsche quoted in A. Weber's *Farewell to European History.*
[3] Ibid.
[4] Burckhardt, quoted in Professor Erich Heller's *Disinherited Mind.*

good. Burckhardt believed in original sin without believing in redemption.

So did T. E. Hulme, who regarded the whole development of civilisation since the renaissance as a mistake based on the false doctrine of human perfectibility, on the belief that ethical values arise from human needs and are not delivered to us by authority, and on a conception of life itself as the measure of all values. Such a society must inevitably decay, said Hulme; and his interpretation of contemporary history is that this is exactly what is happening.[1]

The mistake of all these philosophers of the graveyard is not in feeling that there is a doom on capitalist civilisation, but in failing to realise that the issue is not the death of a culture but the birth pangs of a new order.

[1] T. E. Hulme, *Speculations*.

E

CHAPTER SIX

THE MEANING OF HISTORY

(2) The Historians

MANY historians have little use either for the optimistic or for the pessimistic theories of history. They rightly reject the speculative theories of the idealists on the one hand and the forcing of the facts into preconceived categories on the other. What do they conclude? That there is little to do but to describe the interconnected facts of any given period, showing indeed the mutual relations of ideology, economics and politics, but eschewing any single principle of explanation, any causal determinants or discovery of direction in history. As one writer puts it: "History is a contemplative discipline, and what you ask of your model is an aid to contemplation. It suggests ways of thinking, and questions to ask. It does not satisfy curiosity, or give any final answer to your questions."[1]

H. A. L. Fisher declares that we can discern in history no plot, rhythm or pattern, but merely "one emergency following upon another as wave follows upon wave; we must therefore rule out all generalisations and recognize only the play of the contingent and the unforeseen."[2]

Charles Beard, the American historian, sets out to "dispel the illusion that there could be a science of history embracing the fulness of history, or any large phase of past actuality."[3] The British historian Harold Temperley declares that "the idea that history is a science has perished." There is pretty

[1] R. W. K. Hinton, "Models in History," *The Listener*, February 6th, 1958.
[2] H. A. L. Fisher, *A History of Europe*.
[3] Charles Beard, Presidential Address to the American Historical Association, 1933.

general agreement that the words "cause" and "causality" should be avoided and that where a complicated aggregation of events is concerned the assignment of causation "is at best a highly dubious intellectual operation."[1]

(1) *The Poverty of Empiricism*

In his book *The Open Society and its Enemies*, Professor Popper severely criticises every attempt to formulate a philosophy of history. Plato, Hegel, Marx and Toynbee, in his view, are all guilty of imposing a predetermined fate on man. If there were such a thing as a law of historical development, he argues, there would be nothing left for us to do but to predict the future and fold our hands and await the inevitable. Theories of this kind undermine human responsibility, since if you know that things are bound to happen whatever you do, why bother to fight either for them or against them?

All views of this sort he calls *historicism*, and he regards them as disastrous. We should abandon them and devote ourselves to what he calls "piecemeal social engineering", that is to say to dealing with each practical problem as it arises without any attempt to push history in some pre-determined direction.

There should be no effort to analyse the difficulties and crises of the modern world, to criticise the basic structure of society or to discover the emerging pattern of a new form of social organisation.

This policy, or lack of policy, needs no philosopher to recommend it, seeing that it is the method of all opportunist politicians. It is an unprincipled method at the best of times, but in a period like our own, mere fumbling for the next thing to do without any understanding of the dilemma of modern civilisation is either futile or fatal. Professor Popper is incapable of comprehending that there are sharp turns in history, when merely going on with the old ways, no matter how cunningly, simply will not do; when the only way out is a new way out, and persistence in traditional courses is suicide.

[1] Beard and Vagts, *Theory and Practice in Historical Study*.

(2) *The Road to Serfdom*

Professor Hayek is also opposed to any attempt to control society or to direct historical development in a chosen direction. The only result of this, in his view, will be a form of totalitarian serfdom.[1] He, with Popper, therefore rejects the attempt to formulate a philosophy of history.

Yet this *is* a philosophy of history and a very familiar one, for Hayek, with Adam Smith, believes that if individuals are left free to follow their economic motives the automatically achieved result will be the maximum good of society.

His argument is that we can never know more than the *immediate* effects of our actions; we are almost bound to go wrong if we try to estimate or plan more distant results and particularly if we plan for the future of society. Therefore the sole determinant of our actions should be their immediate profit to ourselves. The competitive market provides us with the occasion for such decisions, but the upshot of the decisions of many individuals taken together is too complex for us ever to understand, so that the end result is unpremeditated. It does, however, in point of fact work out in an automatic achievement of what is socially desirable. Social planning, on the other hand, is impossible and dangerous, and submits us to theories, principles and plans which the human mind ought never to attempt to draw up and which will inevitably land us in evils which were not intended.

Hayek desires above everything a society in which the individual is absolutely free, and he thinks that this will be achieved by the method of *laissez faire* and by avoiding plans and schemes which impose controls on individuals.

But on his own confession the freedom which he advocates *negates itself* and turns out to be the road to that serfdom which he was most anxious to avoid. For the effect of the system which he recommends is, he admits, the appearance of anonymous and irrational forces in society to which the individual must learn to submit in spite of the fact that they

[1] F. A. Hayek, *The Road to Serfdom*.

appear to have no justification and to be irrational and un-intelligible. If people are too individualistic to accept this situation, then the automatic operation of economic law cannot function. It is to be regretted, he says, that the craving for intelligibility produces illusory demands which no such system can satisfy. The demand for conformity to moral principles is evidence of a vicious desire to see all social activity as recognisably part of a coherent plan. Such a demand is to be deprecated.[1]

Thus by Hayek's own showing the rejection of conscious and scientifically planned control in human affairs does not lead to an orderly and stable system but to the appearance of blind forces working contrary to reason and moral principle to crush and destroy the individual. So much for Hayek's philosophy of history.

(3) *Retreat to the Past*

The poverty of historicism as a phrase might well give place to the poverty of empiricism, which is even more obvious in the philosophy of Professor Oakeshott. He admits that in social affairs we must have some kind of policy since "politics without a policy is an approach to lunacy", but policy must on no account be based on an overall philosophy of society which endeavours to discern the trend of events and the pattern of an improved form of society; it must arise from a *post facto* enquiry into the working of the present system and a return to "the unimpaired resources of tradition," excluding any vain anticipations of future betterment or any desire to find guidance for the future.[2]

Traditionalism does not always offer us such scanty fare. There is a more romantic feeling and a somewhat heady optimism in the frank return to conservatism which is now becoming popular in certain circles. Curiously enough, it is in the United States that the return to traditional policies is being most seriously advocated. Russell Kirk, the American political

[1] F. A. Hayek, *Individualism, True and False.*
[2] M. Oakeshott, *Political Education.*

theorist, in his book *The Conservative Mind* exhorts us to return to Burke and Coleridge. Existing institutions, embodying as they do property rights, privileges and minority rule, are the product of slow growth, and therefore embody the ripe fruits of human experience. This is likely to be more trustworthy than any appeal to reason and far more dependable than any guidance obtained from the votes of a mass electorate.

Of course, says Kirk,[1] our aim should be the common good; but this emanates from the providential order of the universe, from piety, from resignation and humility and not from any appeal to the immediate experience of mankind. A natural harmony of diverse interests has been achieved by a series of fine adjustments, a position of equipoise easily upset by utopian theorists or tribunes of the people. The wisdom of the entire human race is embodied in tradition, laws, existing institutions and even in our prejudices. We may not be able to comprehend the established system or justify it intellectually, "but we ought nevertheless to venerate where we are unable to understand."[2]

Kirk eloquently expounds these doctrines, which Burke used to oppose the French Revolution, as just what is desperately needed to-day both in the United States and in Europe to counteract the slide to social chaos.

He then turns to Coleridge, who added to Burke's traditionalism a supernatural sanction. This, too, we need, to hold the frontiers of civilisation against the socialist menace. Coleridge deplored "the reduction of the solemn mystery of life to the sordid principle of the greatest happiness of the greatest number." The right of private judgment means that men will blind themselves to the wisdom of that supernatural government which operates through existing institutions. Once men begin to decide for themselves what is socially desirable they will forget the divine nature of law and the sanctity of tradition.

Kirk concludes that government must be protected from

---

[1] Russell Kirk, *The Conservative Mind*.
[2] Burke's *Reflections on the French Revolution*.

democratic pressure, and the power of the executive must be strengthened. Democracy has some painful lessons to learn, but in the end men will prefer an authority which is paternal to a freedom which threatens to wreck society, and will come to understand that the harder they try to make earth into heaven, the more likely they will be to make it hell.

(4) *History in Reverse Gear*

It might be thought that a philosophy so irrationalist in principle and anti-democratic in spirit could only be a negligible eccentricity of the academic mind. It is much more than that. It is a significant trend in contemporary thinking, especially in the U.S.A., and very widely accepted. It dovetails with recent studies designed to show that American monopoly capitalism is successfully assuming the functions of government, and that an élite of business tycoons and trade union leaders, whose *balance of power* among themselves makes government control unnecessary, can safely be trusted with the authority of government.

At every point the right of the democratic state to interfere with business is being attacked. The academic philosophising is the ideological reinforcement of such attacks.

Theological arguments for man's inadequacy and sinfulness and for the folly of trusting to reason give added support to theories which condemn his presumptuous attempts to control history, and are intended to cure men of their "adolescent infatuation with the idea of controlling nature by science and technology." Philosophy and religion have to teach us to take a humbler and more pious view of human nature, and to restrain our intemperate optimism. Men must learn to be more cautious about human improveability and to put a more sober estimate on schemes to better their social circumstances.[1]

Richard Weaver has been widely accepted in America as a philosophic critic of democratic trends in society, and even in this country he has been the subject of Third Programme

[1] Richard Weaver, *Ideas Have Consequences*.

discussions. He equates empiricism, which is content with mere facts and rejects the reality of underlying laws and principles, with that "unfixing of relationships" which underlies socialism. He advocates what he calls "philosophical realism", by which he means belief in the real existence of absolute principles, which are therefore unconditional and exist prior to and independently of human experience and human needs. Only a system of such fixed principles can provide us with the basis for a hierarchical conception of society which gives every man his place, secures the subordination of inferiors to their natural superiors and holds the community together. Only a metaphysical foundation of this sort provides the necessary authority for property rights and a ruling élite.

If Weaver had attempted any philosophical defence of this position one would be prepared to meet it, but, rather inconsistently for one who opposes rational principle to the bare assertion of fact, the only ground he advances for its acceptance is that it is indispensable for resisting the advance of socialism. It is therefore legitimate to consider his philosophy in relation to the context of its origin and the interests that it serves.

Academic philosophy frequently isolates itself from such inquiry by the claim that it is only concerned with the validity of theory, not its causal origin or actual function. Of course, when theories are supported by rational arguments those arguments should be met, but theories are often almost meaningless unless related to social conflicts. From this point of view the cogency and popularity of the views we have been considering are seen to rest not on their logic but on their ideological role, which is to halt the spread of socialism and stop the onward march of the common people.

From this standpoint much contemporary American philosophy, with its return to absolutism and tradition, its cynical recourse to religious sanctions, and its doctrine of the élite, plainly serves the reactionary purpose of securing capitalist society against the perils of that democracy which exists for the greatest happiness of the greatest number, in which there are no privileges which do not correspond to services, in which men impiously seek to control the world by scientific knowledge and abolish disease and hunger, in which men have equal rights and opportunities and the common man bears the responsibilities of government.

CHAPTER SEVEN

TOWARDS A SCIENCE OF SOCIETY

WE have found that on the one hand attempts to frame a metaphysical or theological theory of society succumb to rational criticism, and on the other that the bankruptcy of a merely empirical approach, with its opportunistic theories of "piecemeal social engineering", is abundantly plain. The third possibility proclaims a blank message of inevitable doom, while the last and most desperate view is so manifestly a reactionary attempt to put the clock back that it hardly merits being treated as a philosophy at all.

Is there anything that can replace such views, or does scepticism finally rule out any theory of history? We have argued that science not only may but must proceed from its data to explanatory theory, and we have sought to show that this procedure is as legitimate in the field of the humanities as it is in the physical and biological sciences. If this is so, is it possible to frame hypotheses to cover the field of social and historical development?

Science Applied to Man and Society

This is indeed possible and necessary. Such a venture will proceed by the normal hypothetical-deductive-experimental method of scientific thinking, adapted to its special subject matter. Naturally, the application of these methods to man and society cannot be expected to give the same precision that is possible in the physical sciences, but it is foolish to demand all or nothing. Scientific approximation is better than unscientific guesswork even if results cannot be as exact as we would wish. This is the case not only in sociology but in biology, medicine and psychology, where the immense value of theories which fall far short of finality and are under constant revision is generally conceded. In every field partial truth based on scientific method is better than a non-scientific approach which removes the whole subject from rational enquiry.

There is a reason for this reluctance to face the results of scientific enquiry—the fear of what prejudice and vested interests might be threatened by it.

only that ?

Science and Life

The first step beyond the chemical and physical takes us into the field of biology, of living organisms, of which man is an example. There have been two tendencies here—a *reductionist* view which was content to express all vital phenomena in terms of chemistry, and a *vitalist* view which drew attention to those phenomena which are not found outside living organisms and attributed them to a vital force or some principle or drive which intervened in and directed the physical process. Neither view is widely held to-day. Biology is content to find a chemico-physical basis for all vital activities so long as the uniqueness of the process is not overlooked. This safeguards the distinctive characteristics of life without attributing it to an alien and intrusive force.

Vitalism used to point to various complex reactions and argue that they clearly indicated a guiding and impelling principle at work: for instance, the blood is always kept at a precise degree of very slight alkalinity, although things are always happening to upset this and the blood could quite easily become too acid. Vitalism wished to explain this by "a balancing principle"; in point of fact it is a perfectly comprehensible buffer reaction which any first-year student of chemistry can understand, and it is entirely automatic. The body is full of self-regulating mechanisms, and all their reactions are explicable in bio-chemical terms and need no vital force.

Now in so far as a bio-chemical explanation is rejected and resort is had to *factor x*, all research is precluded; vitalism is therefore a great hindrance to research. It is the conviction

Nuts

that there *is* a bio-chemical explanation that drives us on in our enquiries. The result has been that vitalism has been driven from one supposedly inexplicable fact to another, in steady retreat. When vitalism has set up some limit, saying—well, all these reactions are bio-chemical but beyond this point *x* comes in, one by one these limits have been passed, e.g. in the factors at work determining the sequence of changes in the development of an embryo from a single cell.

Biology has developed because of the comprehensive theories which have been advanced, discussed, tested by further evidence, discussed again, modified and embodied in the total system. Among these we find not only the theory of evolution, itself a discovery of the first importance, but a number of far-reaching principles proper to the field of biology. These are fundamental to all the work now going on in physiology and medicine, and also to the very practical work of agriculturalists, stock breeders, the fisheries, control of animal pests and parasites—organisms responsible for great economic loss and much preventible disease.

The effective control which biological theory places in our hands is convincing evidence that we have in our hands a science in its own right, though we are dealing with processes basically different from (though dependent upon) those of chemistry and physics.

What is significant for our purpose is the capacity of scientific thought to build up theories of this sort, a system of knowledge which reaches far beyond empirical observation and yet is completely dependent upon it, a system demanding speculative insight and imagination and yet which stands only in so far as it is verified by experiment and observation.

Evolution

The importance of the Darwinian theory was not only that it explained how existing species of animals were descended from more primitive forms, but that it contradicted the generally accepted view of the *permanence* of all natural objects, of their unchangeable nature.

Differences between kinds had for centuries been regarded as a primary fact of nature, but now the speculation of those earlier philosophers who had believed in change received remarkable confirmation from science. In 1809 Lamarck declared that "nature had successively produced the different bodies endowed with life from the simplest worm upwards", an unbroken ladder to which has been added rung after rung until man appeared as the highest form. Finally Darwin concluded that we can no longer look at an organism as something merely given and in its origins beyond comprehension. The study of natural history begins where we regard every production of nature as one which has had a history, when we contemplate every complex structure and instinct as the summing up of many contrivances, each useful to the possessor.

This dealt a heavy blow at the static conception of fixed and immutable entities, each maintaining its uniqueness and incapable of being transformed into anything else, the view which regards the inner essence of anything as defining and determining it, fixing its nature unalterably.

Now there enters the opposite principle—*the dynamic theory of forms*, which held that reality has an intrinsic principle of creativity, of novelty, of adding new things to the sum of being. This undermines the whole idea of a fixed order, of the intrinsically unchangeable. The principle of growth was extended from the earlier notion of each thing attaining its own fixed form to the whole stream of life as it goes on in time. Life itself evolves from simple beginnings to its present vast reach and complexity.

The theory of evolution has been applied in every field—to the development of religion and ethics, of law and art, and above all to society. It means the discovery of the laws of social development, thus revealing the part that human beings can and must play in social change. "Just as Darwin discovered the law of evolution in organic nature, so Marx discovered the law of evolution in human history."[1]

---

[1] Engels, *Speech at the Graveside of Karl Marx.*

Evolution has of course been extended to embrace astronomical objects, the earth itself, the origin of life and the evolution of mind. It accepts a sequence of levels, each unique and each dependent upon those preceding it. Molecules include atoms, but are not atoms, having properties of their own which are different from those of the atoms which constitute them; colloids consist of molecules, but have properties not found in solutions; cells consist of colloids but manifest the properties of living things, such as the ability to build up complex organic substances out of simpler, self-repair, sensitivity and reproduction; organisms consist of cells and organs but maintain an independent, self-sustaining existence.

Aristotle believed in the different levels of existence and even in the dependence of higher levels on lower, but his mind could not have conceived an actual *evolution* of a lower level into a higher. Joad agreed with him: "You cannot from a combination of things, none of which possess a certain quality, produce something which has the quality. You cannot from the combination of non-coloured entities produce colour." The whole point is that you can. Aristotle and Joad are wholly enslaved to the conception of static forms.

But evolution does not merely *register* the successive differences, it believes that the earlier and simpler forms are changed into the later and more complex, that properties and modes of behaviour absent in the earlier stage appear in the later. Moreover, evolution does not attribute this to some extraneous vital force which determines the course of evolutionary development, but to the capacity of *self-change* in relation to the environment, the capacity of things to recreate themselves in a new pattern of organisation, with new organs and new modes of existence.

The doctrine of evolution completed the task already accomplished in the natural sciences, it *banished teleology* from the world of living things; that is to say, instead of postulating an *end pattern* to which things are made to conform, something existing prior to its appearance in its final forms and determining that appearance, it finds the *causes* of development at the level on which the earlier form exists, and in the operation of the laws proper to that level—just as in geology we see that the present landscape, its rivers and mountains and plains and valleys are the product of past conditions, and have not been moulded by a creative hand.

The evolutionary process shows no sign of divine purpose or prevision, and require no purposive intervention. Darwin's theory, though subsequently much modified, showed how causes completely explicable and natural could themselves bring about an evolutionary change. The whole strength of Darwinism and reason for its triumph was its demonstration that new species with new qualities could appear as a result of variation and *natural* selection, without conscious purpose playing any part.

Medicine

Perhaps the most instructive sphere of all for our purpose is medicine, for here we have three clearly marked phases:

(*a*) The magical phase in which supernatural remedies were believed in.

(*b*) The empirical phase in which, without explanation, certain herbal remedies (like digitalis) were known to have a certain effect, and certain practices were held (again without good reason) to be beneficial—water cures, sea-bathing, cupping and so forth.

(*c*) The scientific phase based on physiology (biology), on the germ theory of disease and everything flowing from it, on the discovery of vitamins and hormones, and on psychosomatic medicine.

Harvey was hard put to it to convince the medical profession of the circulation of the blood, which was an inference beyond the empirical evidence. Pasteur and Lister both had to fight hard battles to get the germ theory of disease and antiseptic measures accepted. The whole of medicine depends on theory, and that theory goes beyond physics and chemistry and physiology how ever much it is dependent upon them.

Explanations are never complete, but they do explain. When we find the bacteria responsible for tuberculosis and even when we know how to arrest its progress, we still do not know *why* it acts as it does on lung tissue. Ignorance at this point does not lessen the explanatory significance of the bacterial cause of tuberculosis. It merely pushes the frontier of research farther back, leaving us in a controlling position over a new area of disease. Soon we shall know *why* the bacteria behave as they do, and this will give us more power. But even then further questions will remain. The existence of endless unsolved questions on the fringes of medicine does not detract in any way from the reality of the explanatory *knowledge of areas of reality* beyond the observed data though still, of course, part of the natural world.

It is to be noted that the whole of medicine depends on speculation, intuition, daring hypothesis; but this is not for a moment to be confused with non-scientific speculation and the type of mythological explanation which is simply a gratuitous form of error; for medical hypotheses are *always tested*, rejected, improved and subject to endless revision.

Another important point emerges. A diagnosis or a suggested treatment, while based on sound knowledge, necessarily passes beyond tested knowledge. It is a shot in the dark. It may prove mistaken. It is highly speculative *and intuitive*, (but intuition which is the rapid and subconscious summing up of a multitude of observations and their correlation with wide knowledge and experience). It is none the less completely scientific.

The doctor is like a judge, he hears the evidence but he has to come to his own decision, and he is not in the position of a mechanical engineer who can calculate the stresses and strains of a bridge he is building and predict with almost complete certainty the stability of the structure, or its breaking point. The doctor, like a judge, has himself to weigh the evidence. This is a rational procedure, no matter how much intuition is included, but it is unlike drawing logical conclusions from given premises. The term "rational" has a

wider range of application than what can be established
deductively. A judge has to judge, and so has a doctor. He
has to use discernment. There is no computing machine to do
his work for him. What is required is *insight*.

Now, of course, in most cases the doctor or the surgeon
will speedily discover how far he was right. He may bury his
mistakes, but he will certainly learn from them.

As a further example of insight and speculation unveiling
hidden aspects of reality, demonstrating that medicine is not
merely empirical, consider *malaria*. We have a purely empirical
remedy for this—quinine, and now some brilliantly conceived
synthetic drugs like mepacrine. The discovery of the proto-
zoan parasite, *Plasmodium* which actually penetrates the red
blood corpuscles, the relation of the parasite to the Anopheles
mosquito, and the long and complicated life history of the
organism was all the work of Laveran, Ross and Manson.
This discovery is based on a whole series of intuitions, guesses,
speculations and hypotheses. No logical machine could have
given the result. But every step was none the less checked by
observation and experiment until the deep underlying theory
was shown to be not a mere statement of a particular fact,
like the effect of quinine; not a useful methodological fiction,
like the ether, or like the old theories that treated heat or
electricity as fluids; but a series of *hard facts*, an uncovering of
reality.

Medicine is of particular interest because it is an excellent
combination of theory and practice. There is constant inter-
action between the two, and in fact no sceptical nonsense
about science not grasping reality ever crosses the mind of a
medical man. Oxford philosophy dons may talk about sense-
data as the ultimately known facts, but not the surgeon
operating for a perforated ulcer. Every theoretical position in
medicine impinges directly on medical practice, is tested by it,
and illuminated by it.

Nowhere is it more evident how much we do not know,
nowhere are we more grateful for the fact that we know
so much. The endless vistas of doubtful theory and sheer

F

ignorance are never thought to cast doubt on medicine as a science.[1]

This is important for the question of the scientific validity of sociological theories. Here, too, we can be scientific without being mathematical, or deductive, or restricted to physical certainties. If we accept the scientific validity of medicine we have already in principle accepted the validity of sociology. There can be no reasonable doubt that *medicine is a science*. Acquaintance with a teaching hospital, perusal of medical journals, some familiarity with medical textbooks, discussion with consultants and surgeons, some knowledge of what radiography is doing, in other words any kind of inside knowledge of medicine rules out any doubt on this score, however much we may doubt the capacity of this or that doctor, the efficiency of any particular treatment, or the satisfactory running of the National Health Service.

Anthropology as a Science

Anthropology is particularly instructive as an example of scientific method, because it is a field in which experiment is impossible in most cases and where field observation has to take its place. There is still some place for statistics and measurements (for instance in physical anthropology), but clearly the really important work is entirely beyond physics and chemistry and is completely in the realm of the human and social. This is the field from which the most strenuous efforts have been made to banish scientific method as wholly inappropriate; but in spite of this, Anthropology has its departments in our universities, its field work, its documented studies, its textbooks, its assured results. It is recognised as a science by all competent to judge. But not by the literary propagandists and pseudo-philosophers, who have no competence in the matter. Adopting a "know all" attitude, writing with a good deal of slap-dash confidence and smartness, working in every now and then a technical phrase or two, or

[1] Bernard Shaw, who certainly did so, was prompt enough to submit to full medical treatment whenever his condition required it.

some reference to a well-known name, they easily give to the non-scientific reader the feeling that they genuinely represent considered thought and scientific accuracy in these fields. They are, in fact, completely ignorant of them. They are simply using bits and pieces of misunderstood science to put across anti-humanist, irrational, reactionary propaganda.[1]

Anthropology is the most richly human of the social sciences, and if anywhere science might be expected to lose its grip it would be here. Quite the contrary, anthropology has made tremendous strides in the last fifty years and has emerged from its bookish pre-scientific stage, when Frazer conducted all his studies (valuable though they were), in libraries, and is now firmly established on the basis of elaborate field studies in which trained scientists spend years living with native tribes, learning their language and participating fully and sympathetically in native customs and ways of living.

There are still elements of empiricism: the bare *description* of primitive cultures which renounces any attempt to discover their origins or the possibility of their development into something different, or their relation to parallel cultures, or which finds its explanation of a particular social pattern in psychological or psychiatric terms. Such anthropologists, while most usefully establishing the unity and correlation of all the different aspects of a culture—its marriage customs, morals, mythology, tribal rites and so forth—regard the significance of the whole pattern as obscure and seek for no further correlation with the associated technology, or between industrial development and social development. One gets the impression that a

Heisenberg's

---

[1] A good example is to be found in a long front page review in the *Times Literary Supplement* for January 31st, 1958, in which Heisinger's principle of indeterminacy, about which the writer obviously knows less than nothing, is used to demonstrate that every atom of society is indeterminate and therefore no sociological laws have any validity. In fact indeterminacy does not even invalidate physical laws, quite the contrary, the whole point is that while we may not be able to predict the behaviour of an individual electron we can with absolute certainty predict the behaviour of a large number, so that physical laws remain firmly established. Even on the merest empirical level the same would hold for aggregates of human units even though the behaviour of the individual might be unpredictable.

which? you I'd say!

people chooses, apparently of its own free will, whatever type of social organisation it wishes to have.[1]

Nevertheless, *functionalism* represents a real scientific advance. It is based on the postulate that the customs and institutions of a living society are all interdependent and, in a simple and homogeneous society, constitute a relatively integrated system. Every custom and institution, whatever its history, has a functional value in relation to the whole system —i.e. it is a means to the achievement of personal and collective ends within the limits set by the environment.

Anthropology has already got beyond this descriptive approach. Classifications of types of culture are now being firmly based on regional types of habitat, natural resources and the means of exploiting them. "The securing of food, shelter and survival to a society's members is the most basic function of any culture, since without these no society can survive. It is here that culture is in most intimate contact with the hard facts of the material world. . . . The techniques connected with the satisfaction of these basic biological needs thus become the foundation upon which the whole elaborate superstructure of the culture is reared."[2]

Even more thorough-going is Gordon Childe in his *Archaeological Ages as Technologic Stages* and his other books (especially *Man Makes Himself*).

A valuable impetus was given to scientific anthropology by Lewis H. Morgan.[3] His first contribution was the discovery of the classificatory principle by which a person's collateral kinsfolk are classified with his lineal kinsfolk, so that fathers and uncles go by the same name and hold a very similar position in the extended family. He was the first to show that kinship and family systems have to be considered in relation to the whole social system of a people.

[1] e.g. Ruth Benedict's *Patterns of Culture*.
[2] Ralph Linton, *The Study of Man*, J. Kroeber's *Cultural and Natural Areas of Native North America*.
[3] Morgan, *Ancient Society* (1877). His views on group marriage and matriarchy have not been endorsed by the accumulated field observations of the past thirty years.

Even more important was his discovery that the basis of existence being the mode of subsistence, the successive methods of production are followed by successive forms of social organisation, so that "great epochs of human progress have been identified, more or less directly, with the enlargement of the sources of subsistence." Social evolution is therefore a function of technological evolution. Morgan regarded the production of iron as an event in human experience without a parallel and without an equal. He also saw the close connection between technology, property and social organisation. "Governments, institutions and laws," he wrote, "are simply contrivances for the creation and protection of property."

Anthropology has recently concerned itself with the problems of *acculturation*, the disintegration of primitive tribal life under the impact of Western civilisation and the reconstitution of new types of native society. This has been admirably and sympathetically worked out by Ian Hogbin[1] for New Guinea and Wilson[2] for South Africa.

In two departments, therefore, anthropology carries social science on to new levels. It is concerned not with the existing structure of society, but with the origin, growth, development and decay of society and its institutions. It is in this respect doing for society what the theory of evolution did for biology. It introduces the all-important conceptions of development, transformation, the emergence of the new, the passing away of the old. In doing so it is not merely recording empirically a succession of disconnected phenomena, but seeking for the laws of development, the explanation of these transitions. We see therefore, that science is not only capable of discovering ordered structure but the process of change. Moreover it can do this not only for animal and plant life, but for man, for the development of society, for the development of those human institutions, customs, religious forms, moral codes and art

[1] Ian Hogbin, *Transformation Scene—The Changing Culture of a New Guinea Village*, and also *Social Change*.
[2] Wilson, *Analysis of Social Change*.

forms which go to make up the developing and changing personality of man.

Anthropology does so only by the rigorous use of scientific method. If it declines into empiricism or wanders into mere speculative explanations it gets nowhere and loses all objective significance. It advances, firstly, by the widest possible collection of relevant data, by long continued and exhaustive accumulation of the results of field work; secondly, by bold and imaginative hypotheses, by intuitive leaps to new theories; thirdly, by the checking of these hypotheses against the observed facts and by going to look for more facts in the light of these theories; fourthly, by the most vigorous and ruthless critical discussion among anthropologists.

What emerges is a growing body of assured results, an increasingly hopeful attitude towards the further elucidation of the problems which remain and which are always emerging, and a considerable controversy over a wide range of debatable material and not yet generally accepted theories.

The Dialectics of Scientific Thinking

Throughout this review of scientific method we have seen not only the close connection of empirical observation and theory, but their interaction. You need a preliminary theory to tell you what to look for. But the facts react on the theory to enlarge it, to modify it, even to overthrow it, while the changing theory itself brings to light new and unexpected facts, or by giving rise to new instruments and new techniques even creates new facts. These in turn demand revolutionary changes in theory, in our understanding of the structure of existence. Thus do we penetrate deeper and deeper into objective reality.

Thought must interact with reality to be of significance. Even when research is for years somewhat isolated from the world outside the laboratory and the interaction is to that extent limited, there is always relevance to the wider fields of science and ultimately to the whole of human life. This inter-action is accepted without question in every science, and its importance in biology, medicine, psychology and anthropology is obvious. We may call it, if we like, the unity of theory and practice.

Our knowledge of physiology brings about a modification of our behaviour as to the food we eat and produce, habits of taking exercise, drinking and recreation, methods of securing fresh air and pure water. It even alters our agricultural procedures and determines our crops and our imports.

Medicine not only carries further these changes in behaviour and social life, in housing, agriculture, transport, purity of food and water, but elaborates methods of preventing disease, dealing with infection, safeguarding the health of mothers and babies and fighting malnutrition. We go on to drain swamps, insist on open spaces, limit the number of houses to the acre, lay down regulations for establishing minimum standards for house construction, healthy conditions in factories and safety precautions in mining, transport and industry. Medicine becomes social medicine.

Among the consequences, which themselves demand further social changes are:

1. The increasing longevity of the population which results in the changing proportions of very young and very old persons, increasing the total "load of dependency".

2. More care for the sick, including earlier diagnosis and subsequent treatment in institutions.

3. The cure and prevention of disease in formerly backward colonial areas leading to rapid increase in the population.

The social applications of psychology and anthropology are too obvious and numerous to mention, both in their use and misuse. A narrow, biassed psychology can be used to "adjust" workers to conditions of strain and unemployment, or to justify the limitation of secondary education for 75 per cent of our children. The remedy is better, less biassed psychology and the resolute exposure of the class nature of distorted sciences.

A biassed anthropology may lend itself as an instrument for

dealing tactfully and successfully with "inferior" primitive people and will therefore be taught to district officers. In the event, anthropological forces will have their way with the district officers,[1] and the less biassed and more scientific anthropology will not only explain new trends to a wider life and greater equality, but help considerably in achieving this in the face of the obstruction of outworn traditions.[2]

When we come to the relation of social science to the progress of man, we can see that while there is on the one hand an analysis of the forces making for social change in the past, as in the science of palaeontology, there is also and necessarily, arising out of this, a science of contemporary social change. These are intimately connected. Evolution just happened, but in social medicine we take a hand in controlling things; history shows us a development which men never intended although they were the agents of it, but now, knowing the laws of social development, we become the agents of further social change, which therefore takes a totally new direction from the course it would follow if things continued to happen without conscious direction and control.

We are thus led to the vindication of social science as the highest form of scientific method and as the means by which man not only controls the development of society, but begins for the first time to frame a world view, a philosophy of life, giving purpose and significance to human existence, without recourse to revelation, without some special faculty to unveil the hidden laws of man's existence, without dependence on a Providence, or an irresistible unfolding of the Absolute Idea, without the guidance of absolute and eternal moral principles existing independently of man and exercising their authority over him. In short, we leave behind both the supernatural and metaphysical forms of philosophy, and that upside-down philosophy which denies the possibility of any synthetic world view at all. In their place we have adequate means to construct a science of society.

[1] Peter Worsley, *The Trumpet Shall Sound, a Study of Cargo Cults in Melanesia.*
[2] Smolka, *Fifty Thousand Against the Arctic.*

CHAPTER EIGHT

MARXISM AND SOCIAL DEVELOPMENT

THE Marxist conception of historical development and its laws is an attempt to construct a science of society. It does not pretend to be the intellectual vision of a great plan or design. It is primarily a method of research issuing in action and tested in such action.

oh yeah?

Its principles are not of course discovered *a priori* by considering the nature of things in the abstract, but are derived from the objective study of events and reflect the actual process of the formation and transformation of society.

In contrast to the philosophies of history which we have considered, Marxism is optimistic without recourse to supernatural guarantees or dependence on some irresistible metaphysical principle of social development. It rejects entirely both the notion of Providence and a cyclical determinism hurrying us to inevitable destruction. It is fully aware of the obstacles which self-interest opposes to progress, but it does not attribute these to original sin.

So far from its rejection of mythology and supernaturalism landing it in a hopeless scepticism, it opens the way to a scientific solution of the social problem; meaning by that not a mechanical or a physical solution, not the deliberate rejection of imagination and intuition, not the reduction of morals to self-interest, or contempt for human values, but an approach which bears a higher regard for human beings than many religious persons show, and manifests its genuineness and its effectiveness by substituting for irrational thinking an experimental and not merely a speculative attitude towards all human problems.

A scientific philosophy of history will reject all metaphysical causes, such as the unfolding of the Absolute Idea, or some mysterious necessity carrying humanity through endless cycles of rise and decline, or some supernatural purpose supposed to explain the ordered sequence of events.

Nor will it look *ultimately* to psychological causes—the ideas, passions and emotions of men. The real problem is not the psychological *motives*, which Marxism readily admits, but *how they come to be*. It is never sufficient to postulate these as ultimates. It is obvious that these feelings and attitudes are *variable*; the urgent question is what brings them into being, exaggerates or diminishes them, modifies them to operate in a harmful or a harmless fashion. *When, where and to what extent* do they flourish and become dominant? These questions cannot be explained without introducing conditioning factors —changes in nature or economic organisation or social structure. There can be no history without psychologically motivated behaviour, but these drives and motives are selected by factors which are not psychological but social.

A scientific philosophy of history then, will turn away from transcendental purposes or immanent drives and seek for its controlling conditions in some observable aspect of the physical and social environment.

In the past, materialist thinkers have turned to climatic, racial or geographic factors. Feuerbach even found a dietetic cause for the failure of the 1848 revolution. It was the potato diet of the working classes! "Potato blood can make no revolution", he cried. "Shall we then despair?" he enquires. "Is there no other food stuff which can replace potatoes among the poorer classes and at the same time nurture them to manly vigour and disposition? Yes, there is such a food-stuff, a food-stuff which is the pledge of a better future, which contains the seed of a more thorough revolution. It is beans!"[1]

That food supplies or their lack, geographical conditions

[1] Feuerbach, *Saintliche Werke*, Bd. X.

and climate play an important part in determining social development is undeniable, but that they are not the ultimate cause is seen when we remember the immense difference between the Greeks of 400 B.C. and to-day, though geography and climate remain the same, or the Danish and Norse pirates of Anglo-Saxon times and the peaceable farmers and industrialists of present-day Scandinavia.

The truth of the matter is that it is not nature as we find it that makes man and history. "It is the changes wrought in nature brought about by men, and not nature as such alone, which is the most essential and primary foundations of human thought—man can react upon nature, change it, and create new conditions of existence."[1] It is thought, as it arises out of the changes effected by man, that gives rise to the motives which control human behaviour and make human history.

Technology and Social Progress

One of the great founders of Physical Chemistry, Wilhelm Ostwald, said that "The history of civilisation becomes the history of man's advancing control over energy."[2]

A culture as we find it, at any level, consists of three aspects — the *technological*, the *social* and the *ideological*. The *technological* system is composed of the material, mechanical, physical and chemical instruments, together with the techniques of their use, by means of which man is articulated with his natural habitat. The *social* factor comprises the way in which men organise to use techniques, as expressed in the system of production relations and corresponding institutions. The *ideological* aspect comprises the system of beliefs, magical rites, religious ceremonies, myths, art forms.

The social-economic system and ideology correspond to the level of production techniques. Production must always be carried on within definite relations of production.

[1] Engels, *Dialectics of Nature*.
[2] Ostwald, *The Modern Theory of Energetics*.

Relations of production are relationships between people, determining their respective places in the social organism as a whole. Each individual has his part to play, whether as owner or worker, as exploiter or exploited.

The total structure of any complex society, constituting its unique character, its pattern of culture, rests on the social-economic system, the production relations, from which arise the political and legal system, the various institutions of society, and the morality that guides people in their social life. "Thus the law, the state system and the morality of any given people are determined directly and immediately by its characteristic economic relations. These economic relations also determine—but indirectly and mediately—all the creation of the mind's imagination; art, science, etc."[1]

The Dynamics of Social Development

In the economic life of society there is a distinction to be made between the productive forces and the relations of production within which they operate. As economic life develops within certain relations of production, a point is reached when they became fetters on the further development of production for the satisfaction of the needs of men. When the contradiction becomes sufficiently great, society passes through a period of upheaval and of radical social reorganisation.

In this period not only are the forms of organisation, the institutions of society, brought into line with the expanded forces of production, but new social classes, which have grown up in the old order and whose interests are linked with the most advanced productive forces, take charge of the re-organisation and initiate it.

They do so because they regard as intolerable and dangerous to their very existence and the existence of society, the continued obstruction to economic development for which the old owning and ruling class are responsible.

[1] Plekhanov, *The Materialist Conception of History*.

Social Transformation in the Power Age

The social system of the Power Age, which for 150 years enormously fostered the development of effective energy in industry, whatever social evils accompanied that development, has come to act as a brake upon further advance. The price and profit system stimulated production and technological progress as long as the output could find a market. But, like the earlier socio-economic systems, the new commercialism has revealed its inherent limitations. In our day a variety of contradictions threatens its continued existence. At one time this appears as a failure of consumption, at another as an export problem, yet again as an inflationary or deflationary crisis. It may confront us as the revolt of the colonial peoples or the failure to develop the resources of the African continent; or what may alarm us is lack of resources to develop technical education and a decline in productive enthusiasm among the workers.

In one way or another the social system is strangling the great technological machine of industry and paralysing the body politic. If the social system continues to hold within its unchanging framework our existing technological resources and the commercial rivalries and class conflict which are engendered within our society, then that society will become stabilised in a more or less stagnant form or disintegrate in war and social strife. Should, however, the forces inherent in the new technology and the new classes brought into existence by industrial development be able to surmount and overcome the restriction of the economic and political system, then society can advance towards higher levels.

There is ample evidence that society is embarking upon the latter course. The first phase of the industrial revolution has been completed. The system of free and individual enterprise has long since succumbed to monopoly; monopoly is now facing its own crisis; concentrations of power without public responsibility among those who control vast corporations is no longer compatible with the degree of unity, integrity and purposeful control needed by the world's industry and agriculture to-day.

Marxism sees capitalist production as highly social and involving the co-operation of many individuals in a system where the division of labour and specialisation of function are highly developed. The basis of the institutional structure, on the other hand, is private enterprise and private property. As capitalism advances and the means of production are increasingly concentrated in the hands of the few, the contradiction between the productive forces of society and the capitalist mode of production becomes greater and greater. There is increasing conflict between the forces and the forms which restrict them. The forms, however, are rigid and resist modification because they are artificially preserved beyond the point where they are economically useful by the ruling class whose interests they represent. Gradual evolution, therefore, is impossible; a point is reached where the old restrictive forms must be abolished and give way to new.

Conditions of Social Change

A social system cannot be overthrown arbitrarily; it is not destroyed until the productive forces which it contains are fully developed and burst the shell. And a new society cannot be introduced arbitrarily; it can come only when the conditions for its appearance have been developed in the womb of the old society. The greatest rock of offence in the Marxist theory is the further recognition that the instrument of change to-day can only be the organised working class as it has been developed by capitalism itself and prepared for this struggle by the pressure of the capitalist system over long years. The bourgeoisie themselves formerly rose to power by the defeat of an outworn feudal aristocracy. But revolution to-day spells *their* supersession by a succeeding class, and that is difficult to stomach.

It is important to recognise that this political struggle, and the transition which victory will make possible, is not automatic, but depends entirely on the working class attaining a new level of political consciousness and militancy and being imbued with a sense of its historic mission.

Both workers and other classes in society must experience a profound psychological change before a class victory is possible. Even the ruling class must reach a phase of uncertainty, lack of confidence and confusion of aims. This is because so long as capitalism presents a form of development of the productive forces, and grows strong and develops, "everyone regards it as natural, obvious, right, even as sacred. But gradually old age comes on, decline sets in. People begin to notice that not everything is as splendid about this institution as once they thought. They begin to struggle against it; now it seems unnatural, not sacred but evil, and finally they destroy it."[1]

Thus in the Marxist criticism of society we are not as it were judging the system from outside; it is society itself coming to consciousness. The real criticism of society is society, which by its basic contradictions brings new forms into being. The agent of social change, too, is not a disinterested spectator or social scientist intervening from without, but new classes and forces, new ideas and ideals, above all a new scientific theory, all of which have been developed by the conditions of the social life which they reflect. It is for this reason that they are so powerful, that they are in the long run irresistible.

Is Marxism Scientific?

This theory of history is intended not so much as an interpretation of the past as a guide and inspiration for the future. It is a daring intellectual venture which has won grudging tributes even from its opponents. For instance, Plamenatz says that "Marxism still remains the most important of all systematic and political theories"[2] and Schumpeter acknowledges that to millions Marxism has brought a new meaning to

[1] Plekhanov, *The Materialist Conception of History*.
[2] Plamenatz, *German Marxism and Russian Communism*.

life—a tremendous achievement. But does its strength and importance depend merely on its being what Sorel called "an organising myth", a fiction capable of stirring the emotions and energising the political will?

On the contrary it conforms to the rigid conditions of a scientific theory. That is to say, it is an induction from the facts, and at the same time a powerful instrument for collecting and organising facts, as is every scientific theory. There is nothing unscientific in this. "How odd it is," said Darwin, "that anyone should not see that all observation must be for or against some view, if it is to be of any service."

And of course it is a theory that goes beyond the facts and is by no means apparent to a surface view of historical data. In this respect, too, Marxism is in line with all scientific procedure. "Those who refuse to go beyond fact rarely get as far as fact," said T. H. Huxley. It is, as we have seen, a superficial kind of empiricism which contents itself with merely arranging the facts. Yet for this reason there can never be in Marxist theory (or in any other scientific theory) the force of *logical coercion*—that belongs only to such mathematical deductions as are found in the propositions of Euclid. Like the theory of evolution it can be resisted, if you really want to resist it. And like the theory of evolution, its truth depends on *converging* lines of evidence from a wide variety of circumstances, and on the success with which it is applied to solve historical conundrums.

What is Certainty?

A distinction must always be drawn in these cases between the certainty of the argument and the certainty in the mind considering the argument, which we may call certitude. The question is not whether the evidence is *coercive* but whether it is *sufficient*. There is nothing that will make up our minds for us, that is our responsibility. We *decide* there are sufficient grounds for belief, and are ready to act on it.

Such are the truths on which we stake our lives in medicine;

but even those theories which have been verified by experiment in physical science have a far greater certainty in our minds than in logic, where they must always remain at most highly probable. The fact that we believe that they are absolutely correct, as we have every right to, does not require that they should be in logic absolutely certain. The conclusion is that theories can be proved, but proof is not coercive logic. Proof, for us, is what *justifies* us in believing. Marxism is that kind of truth.

This means that however valuable Marxism may be, it needs continually to be tested by reference to further historical facts as they emerge, and developed in the light of those facts. The revision of a theory need not in any way weaken a theory, it may strengthen it. When we are compelled to modify our views in this way, it is not a defeat for our scientific approach, but a victory; for every old view abandoned implies in such a case that another step of scientific insight has been gained.

Marxism and Dogma

But Marxism may be conceived in a dogmatic form and, claiming too much, lose the assent of critical thinkers.

It may be stated and held as a tight, complete and rigid theory which is incapable of growth and from which no part may be subtracted. The possibility of a "revisionism" which seeks to remove from Marxism some basic principle must not prevent us from developing Marxist theory in the light of experience, new conditions and new possibilities. "Revisionism" and development are very different things. Lenin, Stalin and Mao Tse-tung have developed Marxism by the courageous working out of its basic principles and have thus made it effectual under conditions not foreseen by its founders.

Marxism may be held (mistakenly) to point to an irresistible force ruling over history, leading us to a predetermined end. It may be distorted to mean that men are only driven by economic motives. It may be distorted into *economic determinism*, which holds that the operation of economic forces and the development of economic institutions alone will carry men to the goal of socialism, all *ideas* being but secondary and ineffective, merely derivative from the underlying economic basis. All these and many other misunderstandings or misrepresentations, some honest, some dishonest and inexcusable, are more frequently found among the opponents of Marxism than anywhere else; but Marxists have occasionally given ground for such misconceptions.[1]

well!

Scientific Criticism the Guarantee of Truth

In a recent Brains Trust Dr. Bronowski was explaining how the scientific method of thinking works. No one, he said, can get away with a merely specious argument or with a case that relies on nothing more than the desire of whoever puts it forward to get it accepted, in spite of flaws in the argument and inadequate experimental evidence. We may be sure that any scientific paper will have to run the gauntlet of critical examination by experts, that experiments will be repeated and observations checked. The same is usually the case in history or anthropology or psychology. What emerges from critical examination, argument, further searching for evidence, is either something fairly credible or the exposure of a piece of inadequate work. This sifting and testing process is always going on in science, and where it is going on truth is emerging. Where it is precluded, either because of dogmatism or because the theory is not capable of refutation or verification, we are not in the realm of science at all, but of guess-work and fairy tales.

There can be no truth without free and vigorous criticism. If we discourage critics we shall cut ourselves off from criticism, and if we do that we shall certainly make mistakes. If we want to avoid self-delusion and error, we must create an atmosphere that encourages criticism. Experience is the ultimate test, but we cannot profit by experience if we accept only the evidence that fits the pattern of our preconceived ideas.

[1] A detailed exposure of these mistakes may be found in my *Marxism and the Open Mind*, Ch. II, "Historical Inevitability".

Only, therefore, if we actively encourage criticism and discussion, enquiry and dissent, only if we put a premium upon non-conformity, can we hope to solve the enormously complex problems that confront us in every science and especially in the social sciences.

CHAPTER NINE

MARXISM: THE UNITY OF THEORY AND PRACTICE

WHAT is important about Marxism as a scientific theory is that it is entirely unlike other philosophies of society in the way it relates theory to practice.

When one reads the philosophers, even the best of them, even those whose attitude is most nearly scientific, one finds them assuming that what is desired is an *explanation* of human existence, as if existence were a sort of puzzle. True, in so far as the approach is scientific such an explanation will demand verification, but even so the approach is a strange one if the only purpose of the verification is that we may be *satisfied* with the explanation.

Science has two aspects. It certainly does seek for a more and more comprehensive system linking all phenomena, that is to say, a more satisfactory explanation; but on the other hand we have equal emphasis on the *application* of science to technology, agriculture, medicine, etc. Perhaps medicine is the best example. Doctors do not want a theory to explain disease, as if that in itself would be enough; they want to *cure* and *prevent* disease. They want a theory which will enable them to do that.

There are two quite different kinds of world view. The one is merely explanatory. The other is a guide to action, it is problem-solving thought *in a practical sense*. It is geared to activity all the time. Its attitude is that life is not a problem to be solved, but in our life there are problems of living which we have to surmount, which is quite a different thing. For the scientist and the Marxist scientist, such problems need a theory and cannot be solved *ad hoc*. That is why K. R. Popper is on the wrong track in his views about "social engineering". He has grasped the need for day-to-day practice, but divorces it from a guiding theory, while the speculative philosophers are for an all-embracing theory and have forgotten about day-to-day practice. Nor is it enough to obtain your theory and then go and apply it, as though beliefs could be worked out speculatively and then subsequently applied. The inter-connection of thought and action is much closer than that. We are all the time as practical, as immersed in the struggle with concrete reality, as any philistine with no theory at all, but we are both *making* our theory by this continuous wrestling with reality, and at the same time applying it and testing it. We know in order to go forward to greater mastery of nature, and that is inseparable from a deeper penetration of reality, a more comprehensive, truer knowledge. Truth is mastery, control, something that is always going forward, always surmounting obstacles, always being drastically reconstructed, because present truth finds reality intractable and must be revised. "All meaningful knowledge," says Professor John Macmurray, "is for the sake of action. . . . The significance of all man's theoretical activities lies in the practical field."[1] Marxism has got to loosen philosophy from the grip of the theoretical, and this it does when it shows that theory issues in a practical technique, of which it is the explanation. What matters is not just that our Marxism is true, but what we *do* with our Marxism. It is a tool, but it can only be an effective tool in so far as it is true.

We thus sweep aside all philosophies that assume that there is an ultimate reality which, if we could discover what it was, would solve all our problems and remove all perplexity. The real task of philosophy is to eradicate any such idea—so many philosophical problems are really diseases of the mind to be cured, mental knots to be untied, not perfectly reasonable questions to which answers must be found.

It is not that there are fundamental questions to ask and no fundamental answers to give, but that the *wrong* questions are

[1] John Macmurray, *The Self as Agent*.

being asked. The intellectual battle is just here. It is to persuade people to ask the right questions, to shift the point of view, to modify the whole mode of thought.

Philosophy advances not by continuing previous discussions which have long been bogged down in endless difficulties, but rather by framing the whole problem in different terms. This will most certainly reduce the number of questions which befog and bedevil us. Marxism, on its philosophical side, is a great fog dispeller. When we argue, it is really with the will to transform the entire way of thinking of those who disagree with us.

The Marxian Dialectic

What we have said means that Marxist thought is dialectical, that it is concrete and not abstract. There is no mystery about this, and "dialectic" is not to be comprehended by puzzling over "the negation of negation", or "the interpenetration of opposites", for these Hegelian phrases, though full of truth, are not always the most helpful way of enlightening this generation. There is nothing mysterious about dialectical thinking; in fact, no thinking is much good unless it is dialectical.

The close interpenetration of theory and practice is dialectical; their separation, which is characteristic of so much philosophy, is undialectical and futile.

Or consider the fact which emerges from the study of anthropology: that man is always creating new forms of social organisation, and when he does so the new form makes him a different man.

Thus man makes himself, and remakes himself, by changing his environment, by producing successively different social environments, or conditions of existence. Man is not an unfolding essence, a son of God, a copy of an Ideal Man. There is no deep buried nature of man to determine historical development.

Man makes his own history not by unfolding a predetermined plan, not because he must obey the laws of social evolution or economic determinism, not by seeking to discover and then embody in social life certain eternally true social, ethical or political principles. He makes his history in the endeavour to satisfy his own needs. The means and the methods he successively adopts to satisfy them are determined by the nature of the implements with which he subjugates nature. Every considerable change in his technology is reflected in man's method of organising his system of work, and thus changes the *pattern of social life*, and this, of course, changes the man.

But if all this follows from the ways in which man satisfies his needs, we must note also that human needs are themselves created by the implements with which he subjugates nature. New needs arise on every level of technological advance. They are modified and enlarged by the character of the new environment and the new conditions which man creates for himself. Man in the Stone Age has different needs from medieval man, and men to-day need television sets and vitamins and good films and holidays with pay and well-made clothes and washing machines and modern furniture and all sorts of electrical gadgets.

Let us consider man's choices and how they are determined. An abstract undialectical way of thinking would demand that real choice is to exclude determination of any kind, and determinism is to exclude choice. Yet neither can be understood without the other. Men cannot but choose according to the requirements of the situation, and the necessities inherent in it and the concrete possibilities before them. They choose from the standpoint, views and propensities that are moulded by the objectives they pursue and determined by the most effective ways of securing them. It is our location within the productive process which determines our outlook, but men themselves created that productive process and the outlook created within it impels them to replace it by a better one.

Even as orthodox an historian as Professor Butterfield is indignant at the inexcusable misrepresentations of Marxism on this score. "You have not answered Marxism," he says, "when you have merely answered some mistaken vulgarisation. . . . Marxism offers a corrective to that older view which evaded fundamental problems by seeing history as a field for the activity of disembodied ideas—ideas that were treated as irreducible, that is to say, as being the starting point rather than the consequence of change. . . . The ideas that move men need to be explained by examining their antecedents. Men who work upon history are themselves moulded by it in the first place, conditioned by it even at the moment when they imagine themselves most free, most masterly in their action upon it. But Marx himself knew well enough that it is men who make history—not economic facts."[1] Marx does not mean to say that ideas are mere products. A doctor's diagnosis is determined (we hope) by what is actually wrong with the patient, but it is not a mere mechanical product. Nor is it being argued that ideas do not themselves affect events, reacting back on the very conditions out of which they arose. Effective ideas are those which reveal a correct understanding of the situation which is being considered. Clearly then, one can hold an economic interpretation of history without in any sense denying the efficacy and importance of ideas.

A similar problem arises over motives. Some people require ideas and ideals to descend out of the sky, bearing an authority deriving entirely from themselves or their source. Marx points out that every motive arises in a concrete social situation and reflects one's class position. Does this mean that men are only actuated by economic motives? Nothing could be more absurd, or un-Marxist. The theory is, on the contrary, concerned to explain the role and mechanism of non-economic motives, and the way in which social reality mirrors itself in the individual consciousness. Marxism does not hold that religion, metaphysics, art, ethics and political decisions are reducible to economic *motives*, or are of no importance. It tries to unveil the economic and social conditions which shape them and account for their rise and fall. Their importance is unquestioned—they are for some men the driving force of social

[1] Butterfield, *Christianity and History.*

change without which it could never come about; but they are also the driving force, in other men, of all resistance to social change.

The groups which stand as the representative classes do not necessarily consciously aim at economic ends or express their aspirations in economic terms. On the contrary, class struggles are often fought out in religious or ideological terms which have apparently little or nothing to do with economic questions or with class relationships. In saying this, Marxism is not accusing the religious or philosophical thinker of hypocrisy or of deliberate mystification. What it says is that men who hold certain religious or philosophical views in full honesty may in fact be fighting under their banner in a struggle which in fact has an essentially social and economic content.

This was admirably seen both in the English Revolution of 1640 and the French Revolution of 1790; whatever the motives, the reality was the transference of effective political power to a new industrial and commercial class which found the antiquated social forms and procedures of a more feudal age, especially monarchical control of finance and trade, quite intolerable and hopelessly inappropriate to economic needs. That the ideologies really belonged to different social groupings with different needs is plain enough when we see that it would not be likely that the parliamentarians would be advocating reverence for the ecclesiastical authority behind the Divine Right of Kings or submission to the Bishops; nor would we expect the *status quo* to be defended by a poet who in *Paradise Lost* wins all our admiration for Satan and all our condemnation for the Almighty, in a poem of Promethean revolt.

Subordination and Rebellion

The dialectical approach helps us to understand how it is that a social system which operates favourably upon economic forces at one time may, when these forces have developed, and *because* they have developed, come to restrict their further

advance and cripple them. Thus Marx is the first to pay
tribute to the progressive role of capitalism and the bourgeoisie
during the nineteenth century. "But the material powers in
man's hands have outstripped the existing forms of social and
political organisation. We are living in a period of extreme
decay of the old capitalist order. The traditional forms of
class ownership which once performed a useful and necessary
function to develop production and technique have now
become enemies of productive development and their decaying remains are landing mankind in a morass."[1]

There is a profound recognition in Marxism of the real
meaning of that long period of discipline and subordination
which began with slavery and has continued down to the
present day. This may be described in psychological terms as
the conflict between the reality principle and the pleasure
principle. Reality is the necessity belonging to class rule; in
such a society the search for pleasure is a sin, and guilt attaches
to repressed desires. Nevertheless these repressed desires are
there and will not be denied. The spirit of man is in continuous
revolt. All the prophets are opposed to social oppression and
tyrannical law, but when the prophet is martyred society is
in the position of desiring the liberation he offers, but is
compelled to reject it, because the time is not yet ripe. Therefore we all share the guilt of those who persecute the prophets
and rebel leaders and put them to death. All through history
the ruling class represses with fury the attempt of the oppressed
to secure emancipation. But the succession of ruling groups and
of the economic systems they represent is always increasing
the power to produce, and *at the same time*, and as part of the
same process of social development, brings forward the forces
working to end class domination. Now, at last, technology,
which once demanded subordination and restraint of consumption in order that the productive forces might be developed, operates against these. It requires more freedom,
more equality and unlimited consumption if the wheels of
industry are to be kept revolving. Restriction of demand now,

[1] R. P. Dutt, *The Political and Social Doctrine of Communism*.

for the first time, means a failure of the market and the slowing down of production—in other words economic crisis. At this stage, again for the first time, the interests of exploitation and domination *obstruct* production, arresting and diverting its potentialities.

A non-repressive, non-exploiting society is now possible under the conditions of a mature civilisation. And now the position of the rebel is radically altered. Guilt no longer pertains to rebellion, we are no longer in the position of both desiring liberation but despairingly rejecting its possibility, and grudgingly, resentfully, submitting to our fate, plagued by "sinful" desires we cannot satisfy.

"The excuse of scarcity, which has justified institutionalised repression since its inception, weakens as man's knowledge and control over nature enhances the means for fulfilling human needs with a minimum of toil. Technology operates the *repressive* utilisation of energy."[1]

But the closer the possibility of liberating the people from constraints and exploitation once justified by scarcity and un-developed technology and social organisation, the more desperately do the ruling classes defend themselves against the spectre of a world which could be free.

When the day of liberation dawns the long suppressed pleasure principle comes into its own, now reconciled to the reality principle.

The profound importance of this analysis for the explanation of much religious mythology—the doctrine of original sin and redemption, of many psychological puzzles, and for the explication of poetry and other art forms, is only now being realised. It is along these lines that Marxism discovers its contribution to the cultural problems of our time and to the understanding of literature, music and painting.

Dialectical Materialism and Western Thought

It is not always realised how far Western thought has been affected by Marxist studies, and on the other hand how far

[1] Marcusé, *Eros and Civilisation*.

independent and scientific thinking has carried scholars who are not familiar with Dialectical Materialism in a Marxist direction. As Schumpeter says in his very fair and sympathetic critique of Marxism, "Marx fuses economic history and economics. He was the first economist to see and teach systematically how economic theory may be turned into historic analysis and how the historical narrative may be turned into a rational history."[1]

Since Marx's time historians have been coming over more and more to this basic point of view—sometimes in spite of themselves, sometimes without confessing that the influence of Marx had anything to do with the case.

Even in a civilisation which is still dominated by a capitalist ideology we can discern two divergent tendencies in every field of human thought—in archaeology and anthropology, biology and psychology, in philosophy, religion, literature and art: the one is in the direction of scientific understanding, the other in the direction of obscurantism, mysticism and scepticism.

Social scientists and historians, whether aware of their indebtedness to Marx or not, are now more conscious of the limits set by technology and economic organisation and of the close relation of ideologies to the economic order. While a clear understanding of Marxism would deepen and clarify this realisation, the results even now are apparent in every field of contemporary thought.

[1] Schumpeter, *Socialism, Capitalism and Democracy.*

CHAPTER TEN

WHAT IS MAN?

(1) The Fall of Man

Original Sin

EVERY philosophy, every religion, every political system, represents at bottom a theory of the nature of man. For thousands of years both in the East and in the West a view of human nature prevailed which represents man as possessing a two-fold nature, part angel, part beast, and, that being so, he is exhorted to subdue his lower self, and many of his most wholesome impulses, in order to keep his soul pure, and for that life after death which is so much more important than life before death. This life-denying creed, profoundly suspicious of the joy and glory of life, has for long haunted men, proclaiming that the world is not an adequate theatre for man's efforts, for he belongs to a higher, spiritual order. Unless succoured by divine grace or enabled to escape the entanglements of the flesh by mystical purification, it is impossible for man to achieve perfection. "Evil wells up from the abysmal depths of the corrupt nature of man," as a broadcast preacher put it recently.

The natural life of man with its desires and pleasures thus becomes something to be shunned as evil and degraded, something to be shunned for higher things.

To-day this doctrine is being revived by those who declare that disastrous consequences have resulted from the repudiation of original sin at the Renaissance; since when *humanism* has taken possession of our minds, persuading us that life is the source and measure of all values and that man is fundamentally good, whereas the truth is that man is essentially bad, he is corrupted by absolute and inherent imperfections.

The belief in man's depravity was the basis of medieval civilisation and its ethics; the humanist conception of man, with its emphasis on the acceptance of life and the fulfilment of personality, is the basis of the modern world and the source of its irresistible degeneration. Man's supreme sin to-day, in fact, is his effort to raise himself, without divine aid, to a fuller life.

The Protestant Ethic

The Reformation also laid great stress on the doctrine of original sin; but it stressed, too, the responsibility of the individual for finding his own way to salvation and for personal judgment in interpreting the Bible and applying it to daily life. This served to make men bring an independent judgment to bear on their business problems and increased the power of individual initiative. There was, however, a negative aspect of Puritan ethics which tended to cut men off from wasteful expenditure and worldly pleasure. Forms of indulgence which dissipated both wealth and energy were sternly repressed, thrift, which led to the accumulation of capital, was encouraged, and with it the business virtues of honesty, punctuality and hard work.

The rising business class drew these lessons from Puritanism, but their humbler employees and servants were impressed with the innate evil in man's nature which made it impossible for any man to perform any good deeds. Their reaction was one of submission—to give in to the dispensations of Providence and their betters, no doubt raised to that position by God. Success in business indeed was a sign of spiritual grace and a proof that a man has laboured faithfully in his vocation and that God has blessed his trade. Puritanism thus obligingly harmonised business expediency and religious duty. There is no conflict between them. "Prudence and Piety were always very good friends," says a religious tract of this period.[1] "You may gain enough of both worlds if you mind each in its own place."

[1] Richard Steele, *The Tradesman's Calling* (1684).

Conversely, business failure or inability to get on in the world indicated divine disfavour, no doubt well deserved. Such a man must be a sinner.

The gospel of self-denial and sacrifice in its most drastic form is clearly meant for those whose economic situation does not allow them any happiness. Here is a religious sanction for the impoverished life, based upon the doctrine that good living is the sign of a lost soul.

Thus Protestantism helped to create that curious product, the God-fearing business man, who works like a slave, and rules like a slave driver in accumulating money which his tastes and his principles forbid him to enjoy, and about the value of which to himself or others he asks no questions. No system of religious thought and no type of man was ever so effectual in promoting that kind of progress which is measured by the accumulation of money. If you can convince a nation that steady industry in profitable enterprise is eminently pleasing to God, but that almost all ways of spending money unproductively are wrong, that nation is likely to become very rich, and to attribute its success to the manifest favour of the Lord. All this was the will of God—and more. In 1776 one of the new individualist philosophers asserted that an unseen hand would guide these efforts at individual money-making to a socially desirable result. What was best for the individual would automatically work to the social good.

> "Thus God and Nature formed the general frame
> And bade self-love and social be the same."

Social Darwinism

Less than a hundred years later Darwin and Spencer brought powerful support for the theory of competitive individualism from the field of biology. It was now believed that ruthless struggle between individuals, with the total elimination of the loser, brought about "the survival of the fittest". This was at once applied to the economic sphere, where it reinforced capitalist individualism. The result was the hardening and consolidation of the new man—"man as a beast of prey". The new man made the New World, and has become the dominant type of the leading capitalist country in our day—the United States. Here contemporary Protestantism lends full ideological and moral support to American business ideals.

The Cult of Evil

This conception of original sin, and in particular the view that the very essence of sin is man's struggle to achieve human satisfactions and to achieve them by his own power, while it finds systematic and dogmatic expression in theology and some support from a distorted Darwinism, is also becoming the very climate of thought in the world of writers, broadcasters, poets and thinkers. Critics of contemporary literature are constantly drawing attention to "the helpless, despairing disgust with life in our time", which they find in so many novels, poems and plays. What impresses them about the characters in current fiction is that "all these people are lost, the corrupt and the innocent together." A film critic points out that the picture of the American soldier in recent films and novels shows him to be "an ignorant, lecherous, drunken creature who—even in peacetime—would see his comrade bullied into insensibility and death yet not raise one voice of protest." It is thus incessantly dinned into us that we are worthless, morally feeble, basically corrupt and incapable of behaving decently.

To the sensitive mind, aware of the menace of things in such a world but unable to understand what is happening, an appalling feeling of guilt and apprehension takes possession of the spirit. It would be superficial to laugh this off as an attack of nerves. It is a genuine symptom of a sick world and reflects more accurately than a careless optimism the deep-seated disease of modern society. Koestler has told us that the world to-day can be divided into two groups—the laughing multitude and the screaming few. What it feels like to belong to the second category we can gather from Connolly's *The*

Unquiet Grave. "Beneath the mask of selfish tranquillity nothing exists except bitterness and boredom. . . . When I contemplate the accumulation of guilt and remorse which, like a garbage-can, I carry through life, I feel Man to be of all living things the most biologically incompetent and ill-organised. Why has he acquired a seventy-year's life span only to poison it incurably by the mere being of himself? Why has he thrown conscience, like a dead rat, to putrefy in the well? It is surely in our nature as human beings to realise ourselves, yet there remains this deadly flaw by which we feel most guilty when we are most confidently human, and are most to be pitied when we are most successful. When did the ego begin to stink? Those of us who were brought up as Christians and who have lost our faith have retained the Christian sense of sin without the saving belief in redemption. This poisons our thoughts and so paralyses us in action."[1]

The Existentialists

The Existentialist movement has made the same discovery. Here, too, we find not a wanton mood of pessimism but a perfectly correct evaluation of the human condition if there is no cause to live for, if there is no comradeship in changing the world, if the working-class movement is despised and socialism is feared.

The Existentialist is acutely aware of the human condition. He rightly declares that there is no purpose or providence outside the world, but only the purposes that men themselves make. This is terrifying *if there is only the anarchism of conflicting individual aims.* But it is not terrifying or an occasion for despair if our purpose is human emancipation as that is rendered necessary and possible by the development of society, and of a new political consciousness which can begin to steer the world for the first time in its history.

Again, the Existentialist is rightly determined to break away from "the depersonalised mass", immersed in contemporary life. This reaction from a debased public taste is

[1] Palinurus (Cyril Connolly), *The Unquiet Grave.*

justified. One of the most disturbing features of our society is the robot mind created by advertising, the film, propaganda and the popular press, which are responsible for the shallowness and thoughtlessness of so much of contemporary life.

But what is the Existentialist answer? Merely to "be yourself" while doing nothing in particular, a sort of passive anarchism. To be a free man, but without hands—mutilated. This is the philosophy of a discouraged, bewildered and immobilised group, and it reflects one of the many aspects of bourgeois decadence.

The Tragic Vision

Whether they be artists or poets, psychologists or philosophers, men of religion or social reformers, numbers of thoughtful people to-day are aware of the repressions and frustrations of modern society and of the distorted human soul which results from this.

They see history as an arena of frustration and incompleteness where social change never realises its aims and man's endless struggle is a terrible process of disillusionment and frustration of all his hopes and dreams. This they attribute to an element of corruption in the whole historic process and especially in all revolutionary movements. Thus they have come to doubt the possibility of the fulfilment of the historic process in time. The tired waves which vainly break on the shores of man's existence not only do not *seem* their painful inch to gain; they do not *in fact* gain an inch. This, in their view, is the bankruptcy of the secular illusion.

The most fundamental thing about this attitude is the pessimistic estimate of human nature as *in itself corrupt*, and by its own power unable to accomplish human aims in history. We have here a purely metaphysical view of the human essence as not constructed by the ensemble of social relations but existing in itself, in the abstract, and unalterable. It is for this reason that every desire to move beyond the contradictions of history or to eliminate its evils must be abandoned.

Theology and the Social Crisis

And then, faced with this depressing spectacle of bitterness and boredom, of guilt and irresponsibility, of narrow aims and petty ambitions, the theologians (who have more broadcasting hours allotted to them than any other kind of teacher or propagandist) come forward with a metaphysical explanation. It has to be this way because our nature is corrupt.

Is it surprising that a good many thoughtful people holding no theological views are prepared to accept the dogma of original sin, to subscribe to it, to adopt the phrase and the theory and proclaim it to the world? It thus enters into all our thinking as a view of human nature which makes the improvement of the human race a hopeless task. But it is important to realise that not the slightest attempt is made to prove this doctrine of original sin. In so far as theology comes in at all it is as a mixture of pure dogmatism, the appeal to revelation, or the most unconvincing and illogical kind of rationalisation; merely a pictorial and mythological way of stating a *fact*. The real reason for believing it is that it answers to the picture of human corruption that we see all around us. Or we could put it thus: The Church has always declared that one of its basic revelations is that human nature is corrupt. Look at man as he is! The Church is right.

"Explanations" of this sort are, however, not acceptable. This is not the way we proceed when thinking rigorously. On the contrary, this is thinking superstitiously. When a savage accounts for sickness and accident by asserting that an enemy has bewitched him, it is quite possible to say: If black magic were a fact this would explain these events. Similarly, it is quite possible to say: If man is by nature corrupt that would explain a great deal. Both arguments are illegitimate.

Science and Sin

Human faults can be explained in quite other ways, which do not invoke the supernatural or mysterious, which are in full harmony with known scientific laws and which can be rigorously tested. Modern psychology has analysed the difficulties which confront the normal developments of character from infancy, with its inevitable demand for the gratification of all desires, to the balanced ego. Psychology has indicated the many ways in which character training can go astray or development may be arrested, and also the social conditions and parental influences necessary for the achievement of normality.

We are aware of the immense importance of the social environment for character and the irresistible pressure in the direction of aggression and selfishness where legitimate interests are obstructed by poverty, unemployment or inequality of opportunity. In consequence we do not attribute human evil to a perverted will, but, finding its causes, set to work to eliminate them by better education and parental care, by the provision of a normal social environment, by removing injustice and frustration. There is no doubt at all that human nature is capable of improvement, that normal, personal development is attainable and that men and women can achieve happy, contented and well-rounded personalities.

There is truth in the contention that a great many people are corrupt and selfish, and it would be as great a mistake to imagine that men were naturally good as to suppose that they are naturally evil. They are neither. They are what their training and self-discipline, their environment and social pressure make them.

Marxism and Human Nature

The Marxist goes farther. Capitalism was always a struggle for existence in which only the fittest survived and its ethics those of the jungle. But as its contradictions increase and its corruption deepens so its virtues—and capitalism had, in its period of expansion, many virtues—decline.

It is to-day a society in which the attainment of material riches is the supreme object of human endeavour and the final criterion of human success. It is the negation of any system of thought or morals which can be described as really human. "It is that whole system of appetites and values with its deification of the life of snatching to hoard, and hoarding to snatch, which, however, leaves a taste as of ashes on the lips of a civilisation which has brought to the conquest of its material environment resources unknown in earlier years, but which has not yet learned to master itself."[1]

The Marxist analysis rejects the cynical view that man is a beast of prey, but accepts the fact that under capitalism he is encouraged to be one and may well think that his only course is to fight for himself against all comers. But the Marxist not only relates this type of conduct to the pressure of a competitive system, it derives the opposite tendency to brotherhood and mutual aid from the ultimate necessities of human existence. It points out that society could not exist without it, that again and again the community is only saved from destruction by setting this principle above sectional interests, and whole groups have learned that it is only through banding together in trade unions and political parties that they can avoid destruction. Marxists believe that although a competitive system has served a certain historical purpose, it has now created more difficulties and perils than advantages, so that the field is set for a reorganisation of society on co-operative lines. The realisation of the necessity of this will hardly dawn on the capitalist class, but it will become clearer and clearer to the workers, to the colonial peoples and to growing sections of the general community. Nothing less than such a basic transformation of the social pattern, and the system of relations within it, will create the possibility of yet another drastic alteration in the nature of man. Yet if his nature has been as radically altered as it has through the successive epochs of world history hitherto, there is every reason to expect a further modification to bring man's habits, standards and behaviour into line with the needs of a new type of human production and life.

What we are witnessing at present is the disintegration of the pattern which man began to construct in the seventeenth

[1] R. H. Tawney, *Religion and the Rise of Capitalism.*

century and which reached its highest point of development two hundred years later. The phenomena attending the breakdown of one system and the birth of another are disconcerting. Particularly to those who cannot or will not envisage any further development in man, the spectacle can only be terrifying. It shows the steady breakdown of existing moral standards, the dissipation of what were once thought to be absolute principles, a profound uncertainty as to the future. This shifting of landmarks and disappearance of standards is accompanied by a breakdown of morals, areas and periods of license, reckless despair, wild search for pleasure, excitement, danger and even death. This is the period in which the psycho-analyst discovers the existence of the death wish, which he regards as a permanent feature of the human psyche. But whether it is human wickedness, or disillusionment and anxiety, or the death wish, these things do not belong to human nature as such but to man in an age of transition, man unwilling to face the future or to contemplate the social changes required, and for that reason confronted with the dilemma of no future on the one hand and social breakdown in the present on the other.

It is in such circumstances that the human condition is rationalised and explained by a whole series of myths, theologies and philosophies, none of them scientific, none of them capable of being verified, and all of them expressing paralysis and despair and contributing powerfully to the ultimate collapse of the system they reflect and the class whose ideology they represent.

It is clear then that the doctrine of original sin reflects not the metaphysical essence of man, but the nature and dilemma of many men in a declining capitalist society. Human nature, however, is not fixed in evil. It is always changing; it is a variable quantity and depends on the particular complex of relations and conditions in which men find themselves. Marxists believe that by changing conditions men may be changed. They believe neither in the inherent badness nor the inherent goodness of man in the abstract. Hulme was quite wrong in attributing to the Renaissance the view that man is already and in his essential nature perfect. Of course if this view were held, it could easily be refuted and then, by the usual controversial trick, the doctrine of man as inherently bad presented as if we had only the choice between these two alternatives: both of which in point of fact are false.

The theologian's complaint is that man sins by attempting to transcend his present limits and by relying on his own efforts to do so. We reply that this is man's glory and the real essence of his manhood. We repudiate this doctrine as an intrinsically sceptical, cynical and pessimistic view of human nature.

Man's Perfectibility

The Marxist view, however, does not for a moment assume that because man is not in his very nature corrupt therefore he can be improved merely by preaching a higher moral ideal. That, in the words of the newspaper poet: "Just the act of being kind is all this sad world needs."

We must not despise this cheerful philistinism. There is at any rate nothing jaundiced or morbid about it, and the extremer doctrines of human depravity are indeed refuted by our common experience of human friendliness and the great reserves of honesty, responsibility and common fidelity without which no society could endure for a day. It is this immense capacity for disciplined co-operative living that is indeed the hope of the world. But this attitude lays us open to all the jibes of the "realist" and strengthens his position, because when it is realised that this type of optimism is impossible the tendency is to surrender to complete disillusionment and the field is left to the cynic.

No philosophy which simply ignores Auschwitz, racial persecution in Africa, the callous exploitation of the backward colonial countries, the atomic destruction of Nagasaki and Hiroshima, the sink of corruption in our own West End (and now in the East End), the sickening story of American gangsterdom, of American social corruption and the sordid worship of money, of the deep corroding pessimism reflected in all our serious novels, plays and poetry, and the hypocrisy, the indifference to injustice and human suffering, the shallow judgments and low standards created by and reflected in the popular press, has really faced the world as it is, the possibility of a sheer failure of our world to face up to its responsibilities, which are great and growing, to the challenge of the immense problems which confront us.

No, when all allowances have been made we must un-hesitatingly reject a superficial optimism and admit that the philosophy which diagnoses man as morally sick and trembles for the future of the race is the more objective, the more realistic.

> "None can usurp this height, the Spirit said,
>   Save those for whom the misery of the World
>   Is misery, and will not let them rest."

The *fact* of human corruption in our society is undeniable, but the philosophy which attributes this to original sin directs attention away from real to mythological causes. Its strength lies in its realisation that it is futile to preach the gospel of loving-kindness in the modern world. Unable, as it is, to see the real cause of this moral impotence, it believes that the force of egoistic impulse is more powerful than any but the most astute psychological analysts and the most rigorous devotees of introspection realise, and that man is the victim of some incurable moral sickness for which there is either a super-natural remedy or none at all.

There is a deeply concealed but much distorted element of truth in this conception of human nature. When it is asserted that it is impossible to eliminate self-interest from human behaviour, and that men will always find reasons for clinging to vested interests, this diagnosis is perfectly correct for a society like our own in which interests necessarily conflict because of its class structure. Socialist society will not auto-matically solve the moral problem by eliminating this basic incompatibility of interests, but it does make the moral task a feasible one for the first time in history. In the capitalist world, on the other hand, because of the insuperable difficulties in achieving the moral ideal we either become hypocrites who pretend to practice an ideal which we betray every day, or we must confess cynically that we know and approve the better but practice the worse, accepting a permanent and hopeless dualism and attributing our failure to original sin.

The Case for Modern Man

The theory that man is by nature evil and powerless to achieve his destiny, that the natural life of man with its desires and pleasures is something to be shunned as evil and degraded, must be rejected.

Firstly, there is the question of our attitude to man's instinctive life. Is it to be permanently suppressed, by law, by the police, by educationalists and parents, by the Church, by employers? Is it something evil, dangerous, a fount of corruption welling up from the depths of man's sinful nature? Are we afraid of it? Clearly it can be destructive, violent, even death-seeking if we cannot find the social channels through which to direct it. The Marxist is not afraid of it and does not wish to suppress it. This is the promise of emancipation and the determining force which gives life its direction. The conflict is not between social discipline and instinct, but between exploitation and instinct. If the repression of exploitation is ended, instinct can freely submit to the discipline of sociality, but against exploitation instinct wars violently and dangerously, and that is why it is feared and why repression is piled on repression in the period of transition. Yet in this "sinful" urge to achieve his destiny, to subdue the world to human purposes, to achieve fullness of life, so passionately reprobated by the priests of our servile state, is the whole potency and promise of man.

Secondly, there is the error of ascribing all our evils to man's splendid endeavour to make the world a better place, to consider life as an end in itself, to grapple with his problems by his own strength and in his own insight. This is to call man's greatest virtue sin, it is a denial and betrayal of man's highest ethical achievement. Of course, this is the philosophy of those who do not want the world to change for the better because that means the end of privilege, disturbance of the *status quo*, the human equality they fear more than anything. This doctrine of original sin, therefore, instead of expressing a peculiarly exalted ethical sense, is evidence of a hopelessly crippled conscience. It emanates from the gravest moral blindness of our times.

Thirdly, we reject the notion that this root of sin, and all the sins to which it gives rise (which can actually be accounted for in a much more rational way) are to be explained not rationally, not scientifically, but by some mysterious cosmic disaster, some vague blot upon the universe which we just cannot imagine away, something also on account of which we must all bow our heads in shame and adopt the religious attitude. This reflects a type of mind which does not want and will not have a scientific explanation of sin. Something supernatural, something paradoxical, something that happened before all time and cannot be expressed in rational terms is appealed to—some explanation more profound than any which the mind of man can understand is postulated as the basic cause of the whole human tragedy.

It would not be correct to say that this leaves us just where we were before, because it does not. It leaves us helpless, bewildered and paralysed; for if this is the cause of evil there is nothing to be done at all. The advance of some theological remedy, of supernatural grace, is really only a face-saving gesture. It has not worked, it does not work, and it will not work, nor is there the slightest evidence for its existence or any convincing explanation of the mode of its operation. The promise of miraculous regeneration is only a gesture, the camouflage of a basic defeatism. It can only persuade people that reform by human effort is impossible and thus paralyse the will.

The world of to-day presents us with a dilemma, reason and

science point to socialism as the only way forward; but this is unwelcome, therefore let us abandon reason and science in social thinking since they are dangerous to the continuance of capitalism. The combination of science, social analysis and the dialectical method sees capitalism as an important phase in human development, but as superseded in due course by socialism and not as the eternal form of human society. Human thought must become revolutionary.

CHAPTER ELEVEN

WHAT IS MAN?

(2) The Ascent of Man

What Makes a Man?

THE view of man as a depraved, fallen and helpless creature can only be maintained if the present condition of man in the Western World is isolated from the historical situation, and the man who is actually part of a complex social whole is considered in abstraction from the forces which make him.

This is always being done. A tortured and rebellious slave is declared to be an example of a degraded type of man. A slum child who is the product of poverty, bad parents, an evil environment, is taken to be bad in himself. A poverty-stricken tribesman from the parched hills of the North-West Frontier in India, who raids the fertile valleys below, is said to be by nature aggressive or a thief.

Such a diagnosis is completely futile because nothing can come of it. It skilfully diverts attention from the real cause of the behaviour and thus leaves us in a false dilemma: either a miraculous redemption, which does not take place, or complete pessimism because man is evil.

Marxism insists that man must be taken in his social and historical milieu, and never in abstraction, in himself alone.

To understand this we must discover man in his origin, in his evolution, in the development of society, in his history.

Man's Beginnings

We must begin with human anthropology and derive the nature and behaviour of primitive man from the conditions of his emergence from the ape-man. Even in the earliest food-gathering and hunting stage man in families and groups organises at least to the degree which protects the mother and her children. Struggle ceases within the group, which has survival value just because it is united and the strong succour the weak.

In such a group traditional techniques are learned and preserved and transmitted. It possesses knowledge, and knowledge is cumulative. Even the most primitive tribe is totally different from the animal pack because its mode of life springs from a traditional technique, an accumulation of devices and tools and customs and useful practices, of annual treks, of expeditions and planned activities, of schemes and arrangements.

Now the character, the nature, the inmost soul of this man is of course a reflection of this society, its rules, its methods of living, its relationships.

And let us particularly note that there is no economic or any other form of determinism about this, for who made this complex society? Man himself, and in making it he re-made himself. He is his own creator.

Note further that even on the primitive level there is built up a strict moral code, a system of reciprocal duties and obligations, imposed restraints, values of human life and property defended by discipline, and elaborate social patterns of mutual aid.

All this becomes built into personal habit, moral code, conscience, attitude to others, behaviour and what we might almost call instinct. Thus is the *character* of man made, and it is a character belonging to the pattern of primitive classless society, not to that of a complex city civilisation, or of a Greek republic, or of medieval Europe, or ancient China, or modern industrialism.

New Ways, New Men

This is only the beginning. We know that with agriculture and the discovery of metals an immense advance takes place and a totally new type of society is constructed and this in turn creates a new type of man, with a new behaviour pattern, new values and moral rules, new thoughts and ideals.

We know also that at this stage society splits into classes, into a ruling and administrative class on the one hand, and the hewers of wood and drawers of water on the other. Is this the fall of man? Or is it an advance? It is of course both. It is the road to the development of the productive forces which in the end makes possible sufficiency and fullness of life for all. It is none the less a degradation both of slave and master. And now there is superimposed upon social morality and co-operation the devaluation of humanity, the corruption of exploitation, the vices of luxury and the vices of misery. Once again man appears in a new image, the image of the kind of society he has made. This is the fall of man, but far from condemning him to perpetual impotence it contains within the catastrophe itself the promise and possibility of subsequent emancipation. Far from condemning man to inevitable frustration it calls upon him to transcend his limitations in the ripeness of time and recover his lost manhood. This is a better destiny than a blind pessimism allows to man. What we are doing is gradually to transform the surface of the globe, to humanise it, to make it over in terms of human purposes. Thus the external environment becomes very largely transformed, with tilled fields, irrigation, roads, cities, mines, industrial plants, extractive industries and a multitude of fabrics, artifacts, new and altered materials (cast iron, steel, planed and moulded wood, plastics, rubber). Thus man masters his environment by producing his own means of subsistence—a vast organisation of machines, plants, transport, economic organisation, technical training, research and the like. Of course man himself is now the reflex and product of his world, he is an engineer, an electrician, a chemist. He bears the imprint of the world he has created. But he is also a functional man, not only man functioning in office or factory, but in a unique system of social relations and in a complex society built on this particular twentieth-century pattern with its ethics, its codes, its values, its advertisements, newspapers, films, books, pictures, novels, churches, broadcasters, laws, philosophies and the whole cultural apparatus which tends to condition us and penetrate to the very core of human personality.

Let us not forget those other functional parts of such an order: its trade unions and dissident minorities, its opposition and revolutionary parties, its poetry and drama of revolt, its cultural expressions of frustration and corruption, of criticism and promise.

Exploitation

It is important to realise that this whole process of development and gradual mastery of the environment is also *a changing pattern of domination, of systems of exploitation; a succession of class societies*. Thus we do not look back to the image of a paradise which man has forfeited by his sin against God but to the appearance in the far distant past of the domination of man by man. And it is here that we have to look for the origins of those human experiences which have been theologically interpreted as original sin, guilt, human rebellion and the fall of man.

All co-operative living at a subsistence level involves discipline, enforced constraint on pleasure, enforced abstinence; but with the emergence of a class society this is imposed by a privileged class, which avoids such constraints, on the class which endures them. This may be rationalised as a punishment for sin. The Old Testament explains the endless labour of primitive society as the consequence of the fall: "In the sweat of thy face shalt thou eat bread. Cursed is the ground for thy sake; in sorrow shalt thou eat of it all the days of thy life."

With Puritanism there begins a new enslavement of the poor under the rising capitalist system, and once again poverty is declared to be clear evidence of moral delinquency while riches are a sign of God's favour and therefore of exceptional virtue. In an age which worshipped property as the foundation of the social order, the mere labourer seemed something less than a full citizen. The rigours of economic exploitation were preached as a public duty and it was inconceivable to the rich that there might be any other cause of poverty than the moral failings of the poor.

The Two-fold Nature of Man

Under every system of exploitation not only is society divided into the elect and those under reprobation, but man is himself a divided personality. On the one side is his fallen nature, and on the other the divine nature that he has lost. Thus man becomes the victim of a dualism, with sordid reality on the one hand and the inaccessible ideal on the other; for man stripped of his dignity is no more than a sinful being, incapable of escaping from his egoism and animality.

Man will never accept this curtailment of his life, and slave revolts, peasant revolts and workers' revolution punctuate the centuries. On the other hand Church, Law and State castigate rebellion as sinful, as an offence not only against one's natural superiors but against God, whom they represent.

The Third Canon of the Church Council of A.D. 358 anathematises those who plead for the abolition of slavery. "If anyone under the pretext of piety, encourages a slave to hold his master in contempt and to refuse to serve him instead of remaining a faithful servant, let him be anathema." St. Augustine puts it plainly enough: "Slavery is willed by God and it is to set oneself up contrary to his will to wish to suppress it." Serfdom was of course fully sanctioned and supported by the Church. "God himself has willed," says the preamble to an Ecclesiastical Act, "that among men some are meant to be lords and the others serfs, in such fashion that it is the duty of the Lords to love God and of the serfs to love and venerate their lords." Finally in the present century a whole series of Papal Encyclicals has firmly put the industrial worker in his place: "The workers shall accept without resentment the place assigned to them by divine Providence". (Quadragesima Anno, 1931.)

The immense authority of Church and society thus stig-
matises resentment, disloyalty and rebellion as sin, and a
powerful psychological influence works on the exploited
classes from childhood to the grave, through priests, teachers
and all their superiors, to inculcate a powerful feeling of guilt
should they feel rebellious, and of humility and subservience
and willing acquiesence in deprivation as their appointed
duty in that state of life to which it has pleased God to
call them.

> "The rich man in his castle
> The poor man at his gate,
> God made them high or lowly
> And ordered their estate."

The ruling class itself, while generally feeling secure and
superior, was not unaffected by guilty feelings too, as the
retreat of the conscience-stricken to the cloister and the
taking of vows of poverty, chastity and obedience indicated.

Now civilisation requires, at this stage, the prohibitions,
constraints and delays in gratification which economic
necessity imposes upon the great majority through the iron
rule of privilege.

Class Struggles in History

But no class remains permanently in the position of power.
One ruling class is replaced by another, thus releasing forces
that forge ahead to establish greater prosperity. Moreover,
in the bourgeois revolutions there appears the promise of a
greater liberation than is actually achieved, the complete
abolition of domination and exploitation. That this is not
achieved means that these revolutions were also betrayed
revolutions and left behind them on the one hand disappointed
and frustrated hopes and on the other repressed guilt disguised
under loud protestations and every kind of self-righteous
justification for the suppression of those who desire to travel
too far and too fast.

The common people, however, perpetually struggle for full

emancipation. To do so they have to overcome the ideological pressure which constantly seeks to convict them of sin when they rebel and to load them with guilt. Religion shows the double tendency of supporting the rich and yet preaching against pride and riches, of reconciling the poor to their lot and yet struggling against oppression as in the communistic sects.

A Non-Repressive Civilisation

But with the immense development of productive resources we enter a new phase. A non-repressive civilisation becomes possible for the first time. It is no longer necessary, because of scarcity, to impose sacrifices on the majority. But this results in a new contradiction appearing in the ruling class. Whereas formerly it could exploit the workers with some legitimate excuse, in the necessity for imposing poverty and restraint on the majority in order to provide for fresh capital expansion, now there is no such excuse and whatever sacrifices the owning class imposes are merely in its own interests.

But these class interests now positively obstruct production and arrest or divert its potentialities. It is no longer true that class rule sustains society as a whole on an expanding scale. As man's knowledge and control over nature enhances the means for fulfilling human needs, the technology which once demanded restriction of consumption now itself demands emancipation.

The pertinent question now is not whether plenty is already achieved but whether a state of civilisation can be reasonably envisaged in which human needs are fulfilled in such a manner and to such an extent that repression can be eliminated. If this is answered in the affirmative, the old social order has now to defend itself against the spectre of a world which could be free, and it does so with a hatred and fury which indicate total mobilisation against the return of the oppressed to equality. Bourgeois man now develops a split personality reflecting the dual nature of his society. He must end up either as a revolutionary or as a neurotic and a hypocrite, persuading himself that there is no injustice, or that poverty is inevitable, or that economic laws cannot be tampered with, or that the moral ideal is being practised satisfactorily enough.

Ideology and Reaction

This is the malaise not of modern man but of bourgeois man, of man wedded to the *status quo* and unable to contemplate a revolutionary change. Revolution is the way out, but it is too high a price for most of our intellectuals to pay.

A civilisation so threatened must take intellectual as well as economic and political defensive measures. Reason and science had been weapons in the hands of the rising bourgeoisie. In the earlier days of capitalist expansion belief in the comprehensibility of things and in scientific progress grew and flourished. But when bourgeois civilisation began to decline and it became increasingly clear that it could not solve the problems created by its own industrial revolution, science and reason became the enemies of the existing social order. Bourgeois civilisation can no longer cope with its own problems, therefore man, nature and human society must appear incomprehensible and uncontrollable. If reason reigns, then the bourgeoisie have to admit their own impotence and bankruptcy; hence reason must be dethroned.

All those whose interests are really or supposedly tied to the decaying civilisation want to believe at this stage in the essential incomprehensibility of things. The old cult of unreason is revived or new ones invented. Superstition is now again waging its defensive battle against science, which again points to the downfall of the old and heralds the advent of the new order. Hence the dichotomy of modern thought into scepticism, defeatism and religious obscurantism on the one hand, and on the other a social philosophy which preserves the integrity and vitality of human thought by laying bare the contradictions of society and calling for radical social reconstruction.

Most of our writers and philosophers are too much a part of capitalism to be able to think in such categories. They reflect the characteristics of their epoch automatically, unconsciously and therefore with perfect fidelity, and since on the only premises they can admit they see in society no way of preventing the destruction of civilisation many of them suppose that there is none. Hence the inevitable dogma of "the permanent predicament of man in relation to his universe"; the problem is held to be static, eternal and insoluble. The particular dilemma of the basic social problem and its hopeless character—on their premises—is enlarged to embrace the whole of humanity in relation to the universe. Thus all those thinkers, whether writers, or philosophers or theologians who find themselves in this position are pessimistic, frustrated and in despair about human nature and the future of the race. For them the greatest sin in all history is the revolt of the slaves. Man's promethean revolt against fate and help-lessness, against exploitation and misery, is condemned as insolent presumption, and his refusal to abdicate the throne of his autonomy as sinful pride.

Manifestly this is nothing more than an ideological rationali-sation of the fear and hatred of the defenders of the *status quo* against the insistent demands and relentless advance of the people. Behind the ethical and theological principles which socialists are accused of outraging stand the particular interests of the privileged. Principles of this sort are constantly insinuated into highly contingent and historical judgments. What goes by the name of religion in the modern world is to a great extent unbridled human self-assertion in religious disguise. As Marx said: "Law, morality, religion are so many bourgeois prejudices behind which lurk in ambush just as many bourgeois interests."

Man Makes Himself

The Marxist view of man escapes the dilemma of the bourgeois intellectual. It is, however, neither a superficial optimism nor does it explain a man-made predicament by the mythology of the fall of man. It sees man making and remaking himself and society. It insists that man should confront authority with reason and think things out for himself, and regards this not as man's original sin, but as his most original virtue. It claims that so far from being helpless without divine aid man alone has the power to change the course of history.

Marxism faces the fact of the existence of a succession of class societies with the distortions of personality and ideology which goes with it. It points to the fact of class struggle both in the past and in the present and sees the hope of the future in the supersession of a class-divided society by a classless society. It means by this not a society with no differences or inequalities among men, with no administration or discipline or leadership, but one in which there is no separate class living entirely by owning, a society where the organisation of economic life is not for the profit of the owners but is planned production for consumption based on co-operative ownership of the means of subsistence.

Such a theory is not a mythology. It invokes no transcendental entities, no mysterious dynamic of history. All the forces operating are open to view, are manifest and objective. Neither on the other hand is it a bare description of the existing economic and social factors, abandoning all attempt at theory; neither again is it the reduction of society to the interplay of mechanical or economic forces.

It is a scientific theory which shows its validity as such by growing out of and embodying all the other sciences, by being a working theory continually tested in action, by being therefore subject to constant revision and amendment in the light of experience, a changing and growing theory (as no mythology ever is).

As such it is a theory of man which alone can provide the basis for a scientific theory of history. Science has put into our hands new and unexpected means both for determining human objectives and for realising them. We and we alone have the responsibility for defining and redefining, for formulating and then reformulating the goal of human progress. We have substituted for our essential "sinfulness as making progress impossible", faith in man's capacity to remake human relations and achieve co-operatively human good. We have substituted for the notion that self-love is incurable the belief that man must realise and is rapidly discovering that social welfare is necessary for self-realisation. We substitute for the notion that we are under the illusion of "premature fulfilment" the affirmation of an indefinite future of indefinite progress. Man rightly seeks to transcend his limits.

INDEX

Man 109 –
God 58 (argi for)
Univ 15

Comm

apol

Phil

Sin 26 – 42 –, 96,
Educ 38, 40
Hist chap 5, 6, 103